THE HILLS OF MARS

By D. R. Haskin

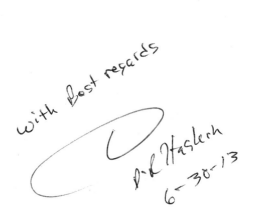

With best regards

D. R. Haskin
6-30-13

Cover illustration by Kimberly Meyer

ISBN: 978-0-615-29522-0

Library of Congress Control Number: 2009904384

Haskin, D. R.
      The hills of Mars / by D.R. Haskin.
      p. cm.
      LCCN 2009904384
      ISBN-13: 978-0-615-29522-0
      ISBN-10: 0-615-29522-3

      1. Haskin, Samuel J., d. 1892. 2. Haskin, Samuel J.,
   d. 1892--Family. 3. Pioneers -Nebraska--Antelope County
   --Biography. 4. Frontier and pioneer life--Nebraska--
   19th century--History. 5. Antelope County (Neb.)--
   History. 6. Nebraska--History, Local. I. Title.

F672.A6H37 2009   978.2'55031'00922
                         QBI09-600066

Printed in the USA
By Morris Publishing®
3212 East Highway 30
Kearney, NE 68847
800-650-7888

For: my family and my Dad – Jimmie O. Haskin.

In Memory of Uncle Fritz.

In honor of: Samuel and Annie Haskin, Wallis and Maria Sophia Haskin, Jap Haskin, and Bill Haskin.

Samuel and Annie Haskin
Photo taken about 1865.
Haskin Family Photo.

ACKNOWLEDGMENTS

There are many people who have helped make this book possible. Many members of the Hubbard, Haskin, and Brandt families have held different pieces to this puzzle, and a family web site has provided the means to bring all those pieces together. So, I would like to thank all my cousins (some I have never even met in person) for posting your photos, news, obituaries, and more on our family site. It has made this project much, much easier.

I wish to thank the following cousins, who provided information and assistance with this project: Pete Hubbard, Alan Hubbard, Ardith Brown, Jera Timmons, LaVon Dike, Jeanette Wietzle, Wilma Reeves, Lottie Faith, Pat Cihlar, Everett and Linda Meyer, Lorene Kinnison, Pete Haskin, Bob and Norma Morrill, and Bernard Raff.

Thank you to my dear friend, Robert J. Gearhart, Jr. Your advice and guidance have always been an inspiration to me. You have always been there for me and supported me through the good times and the bad. Your encouragement helped me through both the research and the writing of this project. Also, thank you for spending several days during your vacation - helping search through old cemeteries.

Thank you to Karl Schultz for reading through this project and for your suggestions.

A big "thank you" goes to Kimberly Meyer, who is a great, great, great granddaughter of Fredrick Brandt. The illustration you drew for the cover of this book captured the character of the hills that surround the Verdigris Creek.

I also wish to thank my great uncle, Bill Haskin, for taking the time to spend with me and show me around the homestead when I was a child. While it may not have seemed so at the time, your stories truly inspired me. Many times, while working on this project, I wished you were still here because I had so many questions.

I wish to thank Uncle Fritz Haskin. I wish you were still

here to see the final result of this project. This homestead, that you owned for so many years, contains so much history. I greatly appreciate you preserving this land and entrusting this legacy to me. You have passed to me, the torch that was lit and once held by Samuel Haskin. I am honored to take on the responsibility of this valuable legacy.

Thank you, Dad (Jim Haskin), for re-telling the stories your grandmother told to you. I wish I had known your grandmother (Maria Sophia Brandt Haskin). She must have been quite a woman.

A special thanks goes to my cousin, Gail Johnson. Your search for our family history has provided many clues to our heritage. Thank you.

What can I say about my cousin, Dee Yeager. I could not have done this without you! You have patiently spent countless hours searching through census records, marriage records, probate records, etc. Your abilities finding information is unsurpassed. Those darn census records are very, very, very hard to read. Yet, somehow, you always manage to find the information relevant to our family. All the times I had something or someone that I could not find, all I had to do was e-mail Dee and she would dig up the information. Dee, you are truly amazing and I greatly appreciate all you have done while researching our family history. THANK YOU!!

And, Thank You, to everyone else who have helped put these pieces into place.

TABLE OF CONTENTS

PHOTOS

MAPS

Raviah Lamora Haskin Rabuck
Photo taken about 1865.
Haskin Family Photo.

Preface

When I was a child, my family would come to the banks of the Verdigris Creek for a family reunion every year on the Fourth of July. At that time, my father's uncles, Jap and Bill Haskin, owned the family homestead. The reunion was a time for the grown-ups to reminisce of days gone by. However, for us kids, it was a great time to play in the creek, look for arrowheads or other artifacts, and explore the hills, woodlands, canyons, and valleys that surrounded the creek.

The memories of those days, long past, still dance vividly in my mind. I enjoyed the adventure of exploring the deep canyons in the hills and wandering through the woodlands. It was always a special treat to come upon the old house, which stood on a hillside overlooking the creek. My father told me that his grandmother had lived there many years before. I could almost imagine what it must have been like to live in that old house. Many questions flooded my mind. However, being just a kid, my attentions were soon drawn elsewhere and those questions remained unasked.

I would also come to the homestead with my father during the late summer when he would help put up prairie hay. During those times, Uncle Bill would show me around the hills and point out the old dugouts and wagon trails. "Shib Carver once lived in this dugout," he would say as he pointed to the oval-shaped depression in the hillside. "This trail went to Norfolk," he told me as we drove along a set of ruts that traversed the pasture.

Bill would also tell me stories of his childhood, but time has wiped them from my memory. How I wish I had recorded those stories. At the time, I did not realize just how important they were. You see, those stories told a history of an entire settlement named Mars. They were tales of people who had lived, loved, sacrificed, and died to provide a future for their children and grandchildren.

Since my childhood, the Haskin Homestead has passed

9

from my father's uncle, Bill, to my uncle, Fritz, then to me. The homestead has been in the Haskin name for 5 generations beginning with my great, great grandfather, Samuel Haskin. As a child, the homestead was my favorite place to be. I never dreamed that I would ever live here on the land that Samuel Haskin settled so many years ago.

Over the years, I have come to have a greater interest in my family's history. It was a history woven into the very fabric of the settlement and development of a portion of Antelope and Knox counties. Several years ago, at the urging of my family, I began researching the history of Mars. The research took me on an incredible journey through stories passed down from the ages. The journey also took me through vast data bases of census records, land records, marriage records, and death records. I also visited numerous cemeteries throughout Nebraska and searched countless numbers of microfilms through endless obituaries.

The discovery of a journal, kept by Samuel Haskin, himself, provided answers to many questions as well as provided a glimpse into the daily activities of life in the 1880's. Once again, the stories began to take form, just as they had when they rolled off the tongue of Bill Haskin so many years before. Gradually, the pieces of the puzzle came together and soon I began the task of compiling them into a written account.

Writing the history of Mars consumed my very existence over the past year. Even as I slept, I dreamed of the people and places that I was writing about. While those dreams, at times, seemed real, I knew that they were only dreams. Then, one night, I had a dream that was so vivid that I was not sure it was a dream at all.

One night, as I slept, I dreamed that I traveled somewhere and met Samuel Haskin. I don't know exactly where it was that I met him, but I know that he did not come here to the homestead to meet me. Somehow, I knew that I was granted only five minutes to speak with Samuel and I had so many questions to ask him. I spent most of the five minutes explaining how I was related to him. During that time, I saw his unique personality -

he was kind of a cross between my Grandfather's brothers, Jap and Elmer. He had a sense of humor and enjoyed a good practical joke, yet he also had a seriousness about him.

It was difficult to explain to him just how I was related because my grandfather was born several years after Samuel's death. Samuel's youngest son Wallis had four children after Samuel died. I told him the names of those children and that the youngest one, Floyd, was my grandfather. At last, he understood how I was related and then asked about his homestead. He seemed pleased to learn that the land was still in the family name.

Finally, I was able to start asking him questions. Just as he was about to answer my first question (What was his second wife's maiden name?), my time with him was up. I felt myself being pulled away from him. "No, no!" I shouted. As I awoke, I was still shouting, "No, no, no!" I sat up in bed and looked around. I was back in my own house and in my own bed. Samuel Haskin was nowhere to be found. I have had many dreams that seemed so real, but I still knew that they were dreams. This, however, did not seem like a dream.

Did I really meet Samuel Haskin? That question kept running through my mind. A couple days later, as I was looking through some records at the Knox County Courthouse, I ran across a marriage record for Samuel and his second wife, Elizabeth. To my amazement, right before my eyes, there was Elizabeth's maiden name. Wow! Had Samuel somehow guided me to that marriage record? Had he answered my question, after all?

I may never know. However, I believe that somehow I did get to meet my great, great grandfather. Despite whether I actually met him or not, I had gained an insight into the man. True, I had read his journal and it gave me a good idea what Samuel was really like, but that dream went beyond what I had learned from his journal. The dream took me deeper into his personality and showed me the immense sadness he held within. It showed me how he had turned his sadness into great pride over the legacy he had created. His legacy is my heritage.

This book tells the story of the legacy Samuel Haskin left to his family. It tells the hardships and the triumphs of pioneers who made many sacrifices to open new lands for settlement. It brings together a part of Nebraska's history that had been scattered throughout hundreds of records, documents, obituaries, and photos spread over several states.

Sometimes, I encountered information that just did not make any sense. For instance, Samuel Haskin moved from Vermont, to Illinois, then to Indiana, and then to Wisconsin. The move from Illinois to Indiana, to me, seemed like backtracking. However, I was able to verify that was exactly what had happened. I don't know why Samuel did that. I have heard a story about his move back to Indiana, but I was unable to prove that it was true, so I did not tell it in this book. Perhaps, that will be a story for a later time.

More than once, while researching this project, I encountered conflicting information. I really wanted everything in this book to be correct and accurate. However, history is only as accurate as the person who is reporting it, and often reflects the perspective of that person. I always tried to verify each bit of information with another source, but sometimes that was not possible. Therefore, I apologize for any inaccuracies or incorrect information. To the best of my knowledge and abilities, the stories contained herein are an accurate account of the settlement and development of Mars, Nebraska. In places where I encountered gaps in the historical record, I tried to remain true to Samuel Haskin's character and drew heavily upon the information contained in his daily journal.

After years of research, here it is. So, sit back, relax, and prepare to follow Samuel Haskin, his family, and his friends as they make a life for themselves in the hills of Mars.

CHAPTER 1 RAVIAH

August 28, 1872, Sauk County, Wisconsin. It was unusually cold and windy for late August, and a mist descended over the Baraboo River valley like a dark shroud over a lonely tomb. A crowd of people gathered around a freshly dug grave in a small cemetery on a hill near LaValle. If one looked to the east from this lonely hill, one could see a small farmstead nestled in the valley near the Baraboo River. Samuel Haskin had purchased that farmstead only 9 years earlier and had given it to his daughter and her husband. Oh, how delighted he had been to give them such a gift. After all, she was his oldest child, his pride and joy. She had married into a good family – the Rabucks. They were a proud German family. Samuel had known them for a long, long time. How happy he had been for her.

There was no delight today – there was no joy. A single tear rolled down his cheek and into the dark, long beard that clothed his face. At 52 years old, Samuel was a very large man, admired by most. He stood 6 foot 2 inches and weighed in at 250 pounds. He had long, dark brown hair and a full beard. His sheer size alone commanded respect. He gave the impression of a man who could handle anything and do anything. No challenge was too great, no weight too heavy, no problem too difficult. He was rarely seen without his pipe. There was no pipe today.

Another tear rolled down his cheek into his dark, shaggy beard. How could this be? She had just turned 28 years old. She was much too young to die. "Oh Raviah, my pride and joy," Samuel thought to himself. He looked over to his wife, Annie, who was standing at his side. Once strikingly lovely, this Mohawk princess now appeared to have aged more than 20 years over the past few days. He remembered how pretty she was the day they were wed. He remembered how angry his parents, Horace and Sara, were when he married Annie. They said that she was a half-breed and no son of theirs was going to marry a half-breed. Therefore, Samuel married Annie, left New York, and never spoke to his parents again. Nevertheless, today, he wished that his parents could have known how happy Annie had made him. She had stood beside him for more than 30 years. She followed him from Vermont, to Illinois, to Indiana, and finally to Wisconsin. Through the good times and the bad, her love and her smile never once wavered. Looking at her today, though, you would never guess that she was the same person. She looked so, so sad and so much older.

His mind drifted back 28 years earlier. It was June 14, 1844 in DeKalb county Illinois. His lovely wife Annie gave birth to a 6 pound, 3 ounce baby girl. Annie named her Raviah, which means "fourth-born." They had hoped for a healthy baby for 3 years now. Three babies had been born to them before, all had come much too early and all three had died. Now this lovely baby was so alive, so healthy. She had dark eyes and dark skin. Just like her mother - a Mohawk Princess. Right away, she was her daddy's pride and joy. She was daddy's little girl.

Although Samuel was very busy operating his general store, behind which he kept his cooper's shop, he always made time for Raviah. Many times, Samuel carried her in his massive arms while serving his customers. Annie always said they were inseparable.

Several months before Raviah's second birthday, Samuel and Annie's second child was born. Raviah was very loving and protective of her little brother, Edwin Ruthvan. Even still, she was her daddy's girl. Samuel taught her the operations of the store. He taught her to hunt, to fish, and to make barrels. She was a slender, active child. Samuel loved watching her play in the street, her long, black hair blowing in the wind.

Raviah also took an interest in her Mohawk heritage. Annie taught her the healing arts of her people and taught her some of the customs. Annie wanted Raviah to understand her native background. Annie was of Mohawk and Dutch descent. Her Dutch ancestors settled west of Albany, New York and mixed with members of the Mohawk tribe. Her family, the

Woodlings, continued to live by the Mohawk ways and followed the Mohawk traditions.

Samuel and Annie moved to Wisconsin with their two children in 1851. At the time, the area was called Marston. It was named after the Marston family who were the first to settle the area. There were very few people in the Marston vacinity in the early 1850's. The land was hilly with plenty of woodland; the Baraboo River wound its way, like a snake, flowing through the rolling hills.

Within a few years, more settlers arrived and Marston became two separate towns called LaValle and Ironton. Samuel Haskin had put in the first general store in Ironton, which was just 3 miles to the south of LaValle, and he knew all of the settlers in the area. Everyone relied on the goods and services that Samuel offered. One day in 1853, a young stranger came into the store. He appeared to be in his mid teens, stood about 5 foot 8 inches, and was of slender build with light brown hair. He was a handsome youth.

"Can I help you?" Samuel inquired, taking his characteristic pipe out of his mouth.

"I am in need of nails, apples, corn, sugar, and flour," the stranger said.

"Haven't seen you in these parts before."

"No. Just moved here last week. My name is Frederick Rabuck."

Samuel helped Frederick with his supplies. He could tell by the stranger's accent that he was from Germany. "Rabuck?" asked Samuel while puffing on his pipe. "Any relation to William Rabuck up at LaValle?"

"Why, yes, he is my older brother," stated Frederick.

Samuel liked this young man. He knew William Rabuck and knew him to be an honest, hard working man. He did not realize, though, that William had a brother. Samuel helped Frederick pack his stuff and Frederick was about to walk out the door when all at once the door burst open.

Raviah was coming home from school and ran into the

store as Frederick was walking out with his goods. It was certainly a meeting neither one of them would ever forget. Frederick opened the door to exit just as Raviah came running through. Nails, apples, flour, sugar, corn, papers, and books flew in every direction. Samuel heard the commotion and looked up from his journal just in time to see Frederick, Raviah, and miscellaneous items strewn across the floor and everything, and I mean everything, covered in flour. Frederick helped the young girl to her feet as Samuel came running from behind the counter.

"Who is this young whirlwind?" Frederick inquired.

With a bashful smile, slightly embarrassed, and brushing the flour from herself, Raviah replied, "I'm, I mean, my name is Raviah."

"Raviah. Would that be your first name or last name?" asked Frederick.

"I'm so sorry," Raviah apologized while attempting to gather up the scattered nails and screws. "Why, it's my first name, of course."

"See you've met my daughter," said Samuel. Then Samuel turned to Raviah, "How many times have I told you not to come crashin' through the door? Now look what you have done!" Samuel put his pipe up to his mouth and took a couple puffs.

"There has been no harm done," Frederick stated as he brushed the flour from his arms and pant legs. "Here, let me help you pick up this stuff." Frederick was laughing, but Samuel did not see the humor in having one of his customers flattened by a 9 year-old bundle of energy. Frederick gathered his supplies as Samuel handed a broom to his daughter. Samuel got Frederick more flour, sugar, and corn. As Frederick was walking out Samuel said, "Let me make up for this. Why don't you come on over for supper tonight? My wife is an excellent cook."

"Well, my sister probably expects me home. She and I live at the old Frasier place."

"Oh, you are over there next to Cyrus Carver," Samuel

said.

"Yep," Frederick replied.

"Bring your sister along," stated Samuel. "We live right in back of the store here."

"All right, then," said Frederick as he was walking out the door.

Samuel and Annie became fast friends with the Rabucks. Frederick was born in Germany in November of 1837. At the age of 16, he came to America with his older sister Sophia Marie. Their older brother William had come to America in 1847 and settled in Sauk County, Wisconsin. So, when Frederick and Sophia came to America in 1853, they too settled in Sauk County Wisconsin.

Samuel was the one who introduced Frederick's sister Sophia Rabuck to another German native that had settled in the area named Fred Brandt, who Sophia later married.

Raviah was thrilled when her brother, Wallis Rowland, was born. She was just 10 years old, but she took every opportunity she could to care for him or rock him to sleep. Annie welcomed the help. Samuel bragged about his little girl to everyone. Although she took on many of the responsibilities to care for little Wallis, she still had time for hunting and fishing with her father. She seemed so much older than she was. She was very mature for her age.

Shortly after Wallis was born, the Haskins left Ironton and moved on to LaValle, which was but three miles to the north. LaValle had become a much larger community than Ironton and was in need of a good cooper and general merchandiser, both of which Samuel was more than willing to provide. The Haskins moved into a large, white house with a maple grove to the east. Samuel then purchased a building on the main street, which he used for his general store and cooper's shop.

Raviah was the one who convinced her parents to adopt a young girl whose parents had been killed in a fire. Raviah was only 12 years old at the time. A cabin north of LaValle caught fire when struck by lightning. Joshua Bailey was able to get his three-year old daughter to safety and ran back to the cabin for his wife. Neither he nor his wife survived. Raviah had been helping Mrs. Bailey with housekeeping during the previous three months and absolutely adored little Nancy Ann. When Nancy Ann's parents died in the fire, Raviah insisted that Samuel and Annie adopt the little girl.

Over the years, the Haskin's, Rabucks, and Brandts all became very close friends. They passed the time in the evenings, especially during the long winters, together playing cards, or dominos. Of course, during the winter they could always count on the Carvers holding a dance at least twice a month. Cyrus and his family always knew how to throw a party with fiddles, song, dance, and drink. During the spring, they helped each other plow the soil, plant the crops, and tend the horses and cattle. During the fall, they could always count on each other to help with the harvest, canning, or even making molasses.

By the time Raviah was 13, she realized that she had a crush on Frederick Rabuck. She wanted to get married, but both Samuel and Frederick agreed that she needed to be older. It was obvious that Frederick had feelings for Raviah, too. Therefore, Samuel made a bargain with him that he could marry Raviah when she turned 15 years of age. The day following her 15th birthday, Raviah Haskin married Frederick Dieterick Rabuck.

They made their home at Ironton. Many times when a neighbor was sick, Raviah was called upon to treat them. It was during those times that she was glad she had learned of the healing powers of roots and herbs. She remembered many of the remedies that her mother had taught to her; she remembered the Mohawk ways of medicine.

Samuel remembered very well Raviah's caring and loving nature. He recalled the night that she was called out to the Wilhelm Meyer house to help Katherine Meyer with a difficult childbirth. Wilhelm had died of fever only 4 months before and Kathcrine had kept the farm despite the fact she was pregnant. However, the farm had taken its toll. She had worn herself down plowing the field. The baby was coming too early. Her eight-year-old son August had run to get Raviah. When Raviah arrived, she saw how weak Katherine was. Raviah did her very best tending to Katherine, using the healing skills handed down from her Mohawk ancestors. Baby Elizabeth was born shortly after midnight and Raviah stayed with the Meyers for two days. However, Katherine was so very weak and she died quietly in her sleep two nights after Elizabeth was born.

Once again, Raviah asked her parents to open their hearts and their home. August and Elizabeth Meyer became part of the Haskin family in 1864. Elizabeth was so tiny, but soon began to grow with Annie's loving care. Raviah knew that Samuel and Annie would be equal to the task of raising these two children.

Raviah and Frederick's first child, Delphine Lamora, was born January 11, 1860. Shortly after the birth of their first child, the Rabucks moved to a farm on the outskirts of LaValle. They rented the farm until 1863, when Samuel purchased it for them.

They had 6 more children in their new home at LaValle. Lenora Amelia was born in 1862, but died when she was only three. George Almon was born in 1863, Emma in 1866, Frederick Jr. in 1868, and then little Samuel (who was named after his grandfather) was born in 1869. Their last child, William (named after his father's brother) was born February 12, 1872. Raviah nearly died while bringing William into this world. She never fully recovered after William's birth. Many days over the next few months, she was very sick and never left her bed. She died on August 26, 1872.

The preacher's eulogy echoed throughout the Resting Grcen Cemetery, but Samuel scarcely noticed. All of his friends and family were gathered around. At his left side stood his wife Annie, Nancy Ann holding Elizabeth's hand, and August. At his right side stood his two sons Wallis Roland who was now 18 years old, and Edwin Ruthvan with his wife, Delia. Next to

August, Frederick Rabuck stood silently with four of his children. Frederick's sister, Sophia Brandt, was holding baby, William. Fred Brandt was holding his own youngest daughter, Anna, who was almost 2 years old. The rest of Fred and Sophia's children (John, Emma, Mary, Charley, Fredrick Jr., Sara, and Maria Sophia) stood next to him.

The preacher finished his eulogy and offered a prayer of comfort. Then, the wooden casket was gently lowered into the earth. Raviah would forever rest next to her little daughter, Lenora, who died seven years earlier. Samuel placed his arm around Annie and drew her close. How would they survive without Raviah? How was Frederick going to raise all those children? It just was not fair. As they were walking away from the grave, Samuel felt an immense hole that gnawed into his very soul, and he knew that their lives would never be the same.

Chapter 2   The Homestead Act

"So goodby Wisconsin with its beautiful landscapes wherever one looks.

"The word Wisconsin, being French, meaning 'where the waters meet.'   Milwaukee, Indian derivation meaning 'a gathering place beside the waters.'   Saulk, from the Indian tribe which inhabited Wisconsin.   Baraboo, French, having been named for John Baribault, who built the first house at the confluence of the Wisconsin and Baraboo rivers.   LaValle, French meaning 'the valley'.

"So now the story changes, due to the Homestead Act, being a law enhanced in 1862, during the Civil War. From time to time the Indian lands were ceded to the United States in exchange for food, clothing, livestock, and money to be supplied at regular intervals. The Sioux tribes finally were transferred to the Pine Ridge and Rosebud Reservations in South Dakota, and their descendants may be found today. They were still wards of the United States for many years, never became self supporting since their hunting grounds were given over to the plow and the cattle range. The white man has not always been wise or fair in his treatment of the Indian.

"Under the provisions of this Homestead Act, the United States Government offered to give 160 acres of land to any settler who would live on it for a period of five years. This was called the Homestead. Then in 1873 the Government tried to encourage the planting of trees by the 'Timber Act.' A man could get 160 acres of land by planting trees and caring for them for 8 years. This was called the Tree Claim. Also there were the Preemptions, which require living on the claim 6 months and paying $2.00 an acre. Thus to a person would be given three quarters of fertile soil which had never felt the blade of the plow share before. Land seekers were going to Dakota from as far back as New York, Vermont, Massachusetts and the middle states. Being the possessor of 480 acres of land seemed more tempting than owning only 80 acres in what was rough country

21

in most parts of Wisconsin. As one South Dakota immigrant expressed himself as being able to put the plow down in the soil and push it for 40 miles without striking a tree, a stump or a stone.

"Thus the Indian Lands gave way to the white settlers."
- Author Unknown.

It was a pleasant, sunny day that dawned over the Baraboo hills that surrounded LaValle. The early March morning seemed more like mid May. It had been a late night. Samuel and Annie's adopted daughter, Nancy Ann Bailey, was married to James Conner from Ironton. Samuel had just finished sweeping off the board sidewalk in front of his store. He placed the broom near the door and took his pipe out of his mouth. He took a pinch of tobacco from the pouch he kept in his shirt pocket, packed it into the bowl of the pipe, and lit it. He took a few puffs and just stood there enjoying the morning. As he looked down the street to the south, he saw Frederick Rabuck with baby William, Sammy, and Frederick Jr. The other children were in school and it was custom for Annie to take care of the younger ones during the day while Frederick worked on his farm. Annie was ready for the arrival of her grandchildren. The two older children ran to the table for their breakfast as Frederick handed William to Annie. As the children ate their breakfast, Samuel and Frederick took their cups of coffee and went outside to enjoy their drinks on the boardwalk.

As Frederick left for his farm, Samuel stood on the boardwalk in front of his store puffing on his pipe and enjoying the fine spring morning. This was the first warm morning the Baraboo valley had seen in some time. Samuel felt like taking a walk. "Annie," he called back in to his wife, "I'll be back shortly."

Annie had just finished feeding Sammy and Frederick, Jr. and was tending to baby William. She walked over to the door with William in her arms. "Don't be long," she said. "The boys want to help you count stores."

Samuel had almost forgotten he had promised Sammy and Frederick, Jr. that they could help him take inventory today. Frederick, the oldest, was going to be five in a few months and he thought that he was old enough to help his grandfather with the store. Sammy, who was just a year younger, was not about to be left out. Samuel knew that they would not be very much help with the inventory, but he enjoyed them nonetheless.

Samuel walked toward the edge of town and towards the cemetery. It had been a couple weeks since he visited the grave of his daughter. Oh, how he missed her. The pain in his heart was still very strong. There were days that he felt as if the pain would consume his very soul. Today was one of those days. Slowly he approached her grave. In his mind, he could still see her and her lovely voice still echoed in his ears. He took his pipe from his mouth and knelt beside her headstone. In silence, he bowed his head and a tear rolled down his cheek. It seemed that each day he missed her more. Many times since her death, he came here hoping, even praying, to find some peace. However, peace did not come. The pain was still there. If he could only have some sign. If there could only be some indication how he could find the peace he sought. Like so many times before, he found no comfort today.

As he rose, he heard a terrible crash from the road. He looked back toward the entrance of the cemetery and saw that a passing wagon had lost a wheel. He placed his pipe back in his mouth and strolled toward the scene. When he reached the wagon, he saw a family of five, mother and father with their three children, gathering around the broken wheel. He had never seen these people before. He knew they were either passing through or they intended to settle nearby.

"Need some help?" Samuel asked of the strangers.

"It appears we're in need of a new wheel," the man replied. "Be there a smithy in that town back there?"

"Sure," answered Samuel. "You folks just passin' through?"

"Government has opened up new land in Dakota

territory," stated the stranger. "Me and my family is goin' to homestead there. If a man is willin' to work the land, they say he can make good in Dakota."

Samuel showed the stranger to the blacksmith shop then helped replace the wagon wheel. By noon, the stranger and his family were on their way in search of new lands to the west. Samuel heard there were lands opening up to the west. He thought about seeking a homestead himself, but he liked it here in Wisconsin. He loved the hills, the woodlands, and the rivers. Yes, this was his home. Still, since Raviah died, he felt restless here. It just did not seem the same without her. He knew that many young and adventurous folks would find the new lands to the west very appealing. He had to admit that he, too, was tempted.

The next week as he was setting on the bench in front of his mercantile, he heard a gunshot from across the street at the saloon. Then he heard some cursing and yelling just before all hell broke loose and someone went flying through the doors.

"Wallis, get out here. There's some trouble at the saloon," Samuel yelled as he began running towards the mayhem.

Wallis was a very large youth. By the time he was 16 years old, he could whip most any man in a fair fight in central Wisconsin. Now at 18, he was even stronger. While not quite as large has his father, folks figured that he was much stronger. He was a good-looking boy and unlike Raviah and his brother Edwin, who were dark skinned and dark haired like their mother, Wallis was fair skinned with sandy hair. At times, he was very hot-tempered and everyone knew that you did not mess with Wallis.

By the time Wallis came through the door of the mercantile, he saw his father rush through the door of the saloon. Without a second thought, Wallis ran after him and entered the building just in time to see his father's massive fist connect with the jaw of some rough looking character that he had never seen before. The stranger's knees buckled and he fell to the floor unconscious. Just then, two more strangers rushed in to grab Samuel. With the pipe still in his mouth, Samuel did not miss a beat. He turned and grabbed one of the assailants and threw him over the bar. Before he could turn around, the other stranger took hold of him from behind. Just then, Wallis placed a heavy hand on the stranger's shoulder. As the stranger turned, the last thing he saw before everything went dark was the large fist of this sandy haired youth.

"Andrew, what was this all about?" enquired the elder Haskin taking a couple puffs on his pipe.

"Them three come in here drunk, got some whiskey, and tried to walk out without paying," the barkeep replied. "Griffith tried to stop 'em but that dark haired one pulled a gun and shot but missed 'im. Then the fat one there done threw him out the door. Me and Gardner tried to stop 'em, Sam, but they were tough ones, they were. Sure glad ya come when ya did."

Samuel gazed at the overturned tables and chairs. Wallis was tending to Gardner who had a gash in his head. Just then, the sheriff walked through the door with William Griffith. "I think these guys need to cool off in the jail," he stated as he was helping them to their feet.

"The fat one's on the floor behind the bar," said Samuel.

"Must be losing your touch, Sam," the sheriff said as he peeked over the bar. "I've seen the time that you would have thrown him clean through the wall. Want to help me get these jokers to the jail?"

After placing the three strangers in their cell, the sheriff hung his keys on the wall peg. "A couple nights in there will cool them off."

"Getting crowded in these parts these days."

"What'd you say, Sam?" asked the sheriff as he set down behind his desk.

"Used to be a quiet town. Now there's just too many people. Strangers comin' in all the time tryin' to start somethin'." Without another word, Samuel put his pipe back into his mouth and walked out the door.

Samuel wanted to check on William Griffith so he headed towards the boarding house that William and his wife Julia operated. As he entered the boarding house, Julia's daughter Media met him at the door. Julia was a widow and re-married to Griffith, and her daughter was staying with them. Media Williams was 24 years old, unmarried, and definitely in the market for a husband. She was not too particular either. In fact, she seemed to have her eyes set on Wallis even though he was much younger.

"Wall with you?" she enquired of Samuel.

"He's back at the store," Samuel said taking a couple puffs on his pipe. "William here?"

"He's in the kitchen."

Samuel smiled and walked through the parlor and towards the kitchen. As Samuel entered the room, Julia looked up and smiled. "William told me you settled a fight."

"There was only three of 'em. Wallis helped." Just then, William came in with his arms full of wood for the stove.

"I see you're no worse for wear," Samuel remarked.

"Little sore, but then I s'pose if man were meant to fly, God would've give him wings."

"You sure flew through those doors."

"They just got a lucky punch on me," stated William.

"Glad you're all right. Too damn crowded here these days. A man can't even walk the street safe." Samuel put his pipe in his mouth, took a puff then said, "Good day William. Julia." Then deep in thought, Samuel headed home.

As he walked up to the door of the mercantile, Gardner was just walking out. Annie had cleaned the cut on his forehead and bandaged him up. "How's the head, John?" asked Samuel.

"Good as new." Then Gardner headed down the street. Samuel took a puff on his pipe and shook his head. "That's one tough kid," Samuel said to himself.

The next few weeks saw more than its share of barroom fights. The sheriff had to hire an extra deputy to help keep the peace. Each night, three or four men had to sleep off their drunkenness in a jail cell. LaValle was experiencing growing pains. Most people were happy with the growth, but some were just feeling a bit crowded. Samuel was among the group of people who were feeling that LaValle was growing too quickly.

On June 3, 1873, Frederick Rabuck married a widow named Mary Belinda Bierd. Mary's first husband, Obediah, had died of fever in 1868. She had three children, Elizabeth, Martha, and William. Samuel was happy that Frederick had found a companion and someone to be a mother to his children. Even though Samuel was happy for Frederick, the wedding made him miss his daughter even more.

Cyrus Carver hosted the wedding dance, which drew a large crowd. All the family, friends, and neighbors came. During the dance, some of the men discussed the Homestead Act. Recently, a number of families had passed through LaValle on their way to Nebraska and Dakota.

"Wonder what the lands are like to the west," Cyrus pondered.

Samuel took his pipe out of his mouth and replied, "A man came through here last week on his way to Illinois to get his family. He found some great land in Dakota. He said it was nice and flat, and no trees as far as an eye can see."

"You know," Cyrus remarked. "I've been thinkin' about headin' on west myself, but I really don't think that I would be able to take all that flat land. No hills, no trees, why, a man would feel naked on land like that."

"I know what you mean," said Samuel.

"Every place we've ever lived has been near a river with nice hills and woodlands where we could hunt," Griffith claimed. The Haskins, Carvers, Griffiths, and most of the rest had been together since New York. Only the Brandts and the Rabucks were newcomers to this group of old friends. Each time, as the population grew, the group would pack up and head for parts less settled. From New York to Vermont, then to Illinois and Indiana, then finally here to Wisconsin, they searched for a place they could settle. Samuel would open a general store and Griffith would open a boarding house. John Brown was a blacksmith, and the rest were farmers, trappers, and hunters. They had all lived here in Wisconsin for more than 20 years. While Samuel could not speak for the rest, he knew that he was longing for a place that was not so crowded. He longed for a perfect place with a river to fish in, woodlands to hunt and trap, and rolling hills with deep valleys to roam. He was now over 50 years old and he wanted a nice, quiet place that he, his children, grandchildren, and all his posterity down through the ages could call their own. He longed for a place that his descendents could tend and care for throughout the generations.

"Dakota isn't the only place with free land." Brown stated in a very frank tone. "What about Nebraska?"

"Ain't it just as flat and boring as Dakota?" asked Griffith.

"I've heard there's lots and lots of grass, but they say along the rivers it's got hills and woods," stated Samuel. "Elizabeth Dalrymple and her sons went there a couple years back. She writes once in a while to let us know how things are goin'. Anyway, she says there's lands near the rivers that ain't been settled yet."

Elizabeth Dalrymple was a widow who Annie Haskin had befriended several years earlier. After the death of her first husband, Lyman Fields, Elizabeth moved to Wisconsin and remarried. Then, she headed west with her three sons, James, Henry, and Charles Fields, after her second husband died. About once a month, she would write back to her friends in Wisconsin. Her letters described, in great detail, life upon the Nebraska prairies.

As Samuel told the men about Elizabeth's letters, they all felt a yearning within to head west. Nebraska seemed to be calling. Perhaps Nebraska would be the place that Samuel actually felt he belonged. Perhaps Nebraska would finally be the perfect place that he could call "home." He was once certain that Wisconsin was the right place for him. Nevertheless, it had become much too crowded and, more importantly, it had become a painful reminder to him how much he missed Raviah. It just did not feel like home anymore. It was time for him to move on.

Wallis Rowland Haskin
Photo taken about 1872.
Haskin Family Photo.

Chapter 3   Scouting the Way

July 1st, 1873 was exceptionally hot and humid in the rolling Baraboo hills. As evening neared, the temperature only seemed to rise. From all parts of LaValle, men were converging on the saloon in the hopes that a shot or two of whiskey would help relieve their discomfort. In the back room, several of the earliest pioneers of LaValle were having a serious discussion about moving west. The meeting was not a long one, but was decisive. Eight men would journey to Nebraska on horseback to seek homesteads. They would take six packhorses of supplies with them. Samuel Haskin, Wallis Haskin, Cyrus Carver and his son Dor, William Griffith, Titus Sherman, Sidney Haskin, and John Brown were selected to seek out land in Nebraska. Edwin Haskin, Fred Brandt, Watts Sherman, and John Gardner would stay behind to take care of the families, farms, and businesses of those who went on ahead.

The eight men would leave on July 5th and would travel across northern Iowa into Dakota, then south to a river town in Nebraska called Niobrara. They figured that with good weather and a little bit of luck that they should be able to get to Nebraska in three or four weeks. They would then scout for land near a river with plenty of hills, trees, and wildlife. If they were able to find what they liked, then they would file claim. Dor Carver and Tite Sherman would remain in Nebraska and the rest would return to Wisconsin for their families. They expected that with a little luck they would be back in Wisconsin by the middle of October.

So, it was decided. Samuel reached into his shirt pocket and pulled out his tobacco pouch. He somehow felt 20 years younger. Once again, he would be settling new land, a task he had done several times before. He had been one of the first in Saulk County as he had been in DeKalb County, Illinois. He knew very well the hardships that lie ahead and he knew the journey to Nebraska would not be an easy one. He felt energized by the prospect of opening up new territory. With a new sense of self and purpose, he took a pinch of tobacco and carefully tucked it into the bowl of his pipe. He placed the pouch back into his pocket, lit his pipe, and took a couple puffs. Then he mused, "You old fart."

"What'd you say, Father?" asked Wallis.

Samuel looked at his son and smiled. "Son, you are about to begin a great adventure."

Wallis nodded his head. He was almost 19 years old and while he had traveled with his Dad to get supplies from Milwaukee and had once gone with his father to Chicago, he still lived within six miles from where he was born. This was indeed going to be a big adventure for him and he could hardly wait to begin. However, there was much to do before they could go. They would need to purchase supplies and pack horses plus review all the maps. Wallis helped his father stock the store and update all the financial books. The young Haskin was very excited about exploring unknown lands, but he knew that he would miss Wisconsin. After all, this was his home. This is where he had grown to adulthood and was the only life he knew. Moreover, there was his girl, Maria Sophia Brandt. She was Fred Brandt's oldest child and Wallis had liked her since they were youngsters. Yes, he would miss Maria Sophia. "One day I am going to marry that girl," he said to himself.

Samuel and Wallis worked very hard the next couple of days getting the store in order. Samuel and Annie's adopted son August would be the man of the house while the men were away. Fred Brandt would help Annie and August and would go on supply runs for them. August's little sister, Elizabeth was determined to help as well. She said that she could sweep, dust, and stock shelves. Samuel had to laugh. In many ways, Elizabeth acted so much like Raviah. Although she was only nine years old, she was very good help at the store.

The morning of July 5th dawned cooler and sunny. It had just rained the day before and the cooler temperature was a welcome relief to the extreme heat that LaValle had experienced over the past week. A large group of people stood outside

Samuel's mercantile to bid the men a safe journey. As the men loaded their packhorses, Samuel reached out to Annie. He gently caressed her hand, smiled, and then gave her a kiss.

"You will find some good land to care for," Annie stated. From Annie's point of view, one did not own land; instead, the land owned them. Annie's views on land stewardship stemmed from her Mohawk heritage. The Mohawk believed that a man belonged to the land that he lived on and cared for. Annie had instilled this belief in her husband and her children, so Samuel just nodded as he walked to his horse. Wallis was already mounted and ready to begin his adventure. He looked over toward Fred and Sophia Brandt, who were standing on the boardwalk in front of the store, and he spotted their daughter, Maria Sophia. He smiled at her as he tipped his hat. Shyly, she smiled back.

With their farewells said, the eight men rode out of LaValle. Soon they were riding through the Baraboo hills west of town and on their way to Nebraska. They made camp the first night just to the east of Reedstown. They had made very good time that day. If they could do as well tomorrow, they would be about 13 miles east of Ferryville. Therefore, they all turned in at sundown because they wanted to get an early start the next day.

As the sun peeked over the Baraboo hills it saw Samuel and his men riding west toward Reedstown and beyond. The group had awakened long before sunrise. Breakfast consisted of jerked beef and coffee. After eating, they wasted no time packing and harnessing the horses to resume their journey. They set a fast walking pace for the horses and every couple of hours they would stop to graze or water their mounts. They stopped about half an hour for lunch, which again was jerked beef. By mid-afternoon, they had come to Reedstown. After an hour of rest and drink, they were once again on their way.

Shortly after 7:00pm, they made camp about 10 miles east of Ferryville. Wallis and Dor went hunting for supper. Rabbit stew tasted great and was a welcome break from the jerked beef they had for breakfast and lunch. After supper, they sat around the campfire talking about the old days when they had first settled Wisconsin. By 10:00 pm, they had unrolled their bedrolls. Once again, they needed to get an early start because they hoped to make Ferryville in time to have a good lunch at the town tavern and then catch the ferry across the mighty Mississippi.

Once again, the morning dawn saw the men already mounted and headed to the west. Arriving in Ferryville just before noon, the men had lunch at the tavern, and then headed down to the ferry landing. They had to wait at the landing for about an hour as the ferry made its way back from the Iowa side of the river. Then it was nearly another hour after they boarded before the ferry was underway. When they reached the Iowa side of the Mississippi, they still had a few hours before supper, so they mounted up and headed west toward Mason City.

They made good time across the northern part of Iowa. For the most part, the land was flat and they averaged between 30 and 35 miles on a good day. The day before the reached Mason City, they had to ride in the rain all day, but it finally stopped shortly after supper. Five days after they had crossed the Mississippi, they rode in to Mason City, Iowa. The men rented hotel rooms for the night, which seemed like a luxury compared to sleeping on the cold, hard ground. Samuel knew he sure enjoyed sleeping in a bed again. Sleeping in bedrolls on the ground was harder on him now than it had been years ago. Even Wallis commented how nice the bed felt.

All the men slept late the next morning. By mid-morning, they were having a large breakfast at the hotel dining room. By noon, they checked out of the hotel and headed for the stable to get their horses. Samuel took some time to gather some information about their route to Nebraska and, shortly after noon, they were riding west again. They would push hard until St. Paul Junction, which Samuel thought they could make in five days barring any unforeseen delays.

A couple days of rain slowed them down a little and they rode into St. Paul Junction, Iowa in the rain on the sixth day after leaving Mason City. The rain had taken its toll on William Griffith. Samuel felt they needed to rest up a few days. They were not very far from Dakota now and from there it was just a short ride into Nebraska. William was anxious to keep moving and he told Samuel that he thought that he would be fine after a good night's rest.

The next morning, after a filling breakfast, William said that he felt much better so they headed toward the Iowa boarder. During the day, Samuel kept a close watch on William. Although his fever was down, Samuel did not think that he looked well. They camped that night on the hills just east of Westfield and woke early the next morning to head into the town. They all had an eerie feeling while riding through Westfield. For the most part, the town was abandoned. As they rode through the dusty streets, they had a feeling they were being watched. Samuel halted the group so he could listen for any signs of life. All he heard was the wind blowing and in the distance, a door swinging open and slamming closed.

"The sooner we leave this place the better," Dor commented briskly.

"Scared of ghosts?" teased Wallis.

Before Dor could respond, an eerie scream echoed through the streets followed by a gunshot. Then several more screams pierced the humid morning air followed by more gunshots. Without comment, Samuel, followed by Cyrus and Wallis, went galloping toward the shots and screams. As the trio turned the corner onto the main street, they saw four Indians on horseback shooting arrows toward what appeared to be the saloon. Someone in the saloon was returning fire. Without stopping, Samuel pulled out his rifle and fired a shot above the heads of the four assailants. The Indians looked toward him and saw three armed men rapidly descending upon them. With one last cry, they turned their horses and quickly retreated from the approaching adversaries.

As the trio rode up to the old saloon, a rather haggard looking man in ragged clothes stepped to the door. "I was in a tight spot until you three showed up," he exclaimed. "Damn devils anyway."

"Why were they attacking you?" asked Samuel.

"They're Indians. They don't need a reason," the man replied. "You new to these parts?"

"We're headed to Nebraska to get some land," remarked Cyrus. Just then, the other men rode up to the saloon.

"What have we here?" Sherman asked. Then, he glanced toward Dor, "A rather scruffy looking ghost."

"Thanks to you, I ain't no ghost," the man chuckled. "Cornelius Owen, folks just call me Owen."

"Where's everyone else?" asked Cyrus.

"Gone," replied Owen. "A couple years back, the Sioux went on the warpath and everybody left. I left, too. I went north for a while, then to Dakota and traveled into Nebraska. I just came out of Nebraska just a couple days ago and thought I'd come here and see if anyone came back. Those damn red devils chased me across the Big Sioux this mornin'. I'd been a goner too if all you hadn't showed up when you did. I'm not goin' to stick around here. I'm headin' east to civilization. If I was y'all, I'd turn around and head back east too."

"No," Samuel remarked placing a pinch of tobacco into the bowl of his pipe. "We're heading into Nebraska. I've bargained peaceful agreements with Indians before. Reckon I can bargain again."

"Yeah," Cyrus laughed. "I done saw you bargain with one the day we left. What kind of bargainin' do you call that anyway - when you kiss one?"

Owen looked puzzled. "He means the man's wife," John Brown stated. "She's part Mohawk and tough as nails when she's riled, too."

"Boy, that's the truth!" Wallis remarked.

Samuel lit his pipe and took a puff. Paying no attention to Cyrus, John, and Wallis, he looked up and asked Owen, "What tribes do we need to expect when we get to Nebraska?"

"Well," Owen replied, "many of the Ponca and Pawnee

36

have been wiped out by disease. Those Sioux have taken advantage of the situation and are makin' raids on what's left. Troops have been tryin' to move the tribes to Indian lands to the south. You're likely to get a very un-friendly reception. They just don't trust us. And I would never trust them. You saw with your own eyes what they tried to do to me."

Samuel looked to the other men. "You heard him. What do you say?"

"I think that I can speak for everyone here," Griffith stated. "We have all seen you bargain with Indians many times before. We came this far and we'll go all the way."

Everyone agreed with Griffith. Samuel knew these men very well and he knew that would be their response. "We go on!" he exclaimed. Then he turned to Owen and said, "You goin' to be alright, then?"

"I'll be fine," Owen replied. "I'm headed east to Des Moines. I figure it's much safer there."

Samuel turned to his men, nodded his head, and turned his horse toward the Big Sioux River and the group was on its way. They crossed the Big Sioux just southwest of town that morning. Their trip through the southeastern part of Dakota was not as easy as it had been through northern Iowa. There were increasingly more hills as they neared Yankton. While the hills were nothing compared to the hills in Wisconsin, they had all become accustomed to traveling over the flat land of northern Iowa. As evening neared, they made their camp 13 miles northeast of Yankton. As before, when they were making camp for the night, Wallis and Dor provided the meal. This night, they feasted on turkey and rabbit. Some nights they had only turkey, other nights was rabbit or even prairie chicken. Wallis and Dor could have easily shot plenty of deer, but that would have been too much meat for this group. Annie had instilled in Wallis that he should never shoot anything if he was not going to eat it. So, Wallis and Dor always bagged the small game. Whether it was turkey, rabbit, or prairie chicken, Cyrus was always up to the task of cooking up a fine tasting meal.

The next afternoon, they rode into Yankton. Samuel had been watching William Griffith and knew that something was wrong.

"Let's find a hotel room," Samuel said. "We'll stay here a couple days so we can get acquainted with some of the merchants. When we settle in Nebraska, we will probably need to get many of our supplies from here." In reality, he felt that William could use a couple days' rest. However, Samuel knew that William would insist upon heading out that very day if he suspected the delay was for his benefit.

Being the Dakota Territorial Capitol, Yankton was a community bustling with culture and excitement. The Missouri River brought steamboats loaded with people, goods, and supplies. While Samuel figured William could use the rest, he felt it would not hurt to acquaint himself with the city. After checking in at a hotel, Samuel headed for the Post Office. He composed a quick note to his wife back in LaValle.

"July the 22 1873
"Der Ann and all:
"Puld in to Yankton Dakota teratory today. Griffith took ill a cupel days back but is feelin fin now. We all are doin fin. We will sta here a cupel days then hed to Nebraska. Will cross river at Nibrary. Will rite you when we find land.
"All my luv, Samuel J. Haskins"

The next two days seemed to fly by. There was so much to see and do. All the men had a great time and the nightlife had its appeal as well. William said that he was feeling much better and all were anxious to reach their destination. So, at the first glimmer of light on the morning of July 25th, the men were all packed and heading west out of Yankton. They camped that night across the river from Niobrara, Nebraska, and the next morning, they caught the ferry and crossed the Missouri.

They stopped at the land office in Niobrara obtaining area maps and information. Samuel learned that the Indians were, for the most part, friendly with the settlers. However, there was tension and there had been some Indian raids. After studying their maps, they continued south following the Niobrara River to the point where the Niobrara turned to the west and the Verdigris River flowed into it from the south. From there, they followed the Verdigris River south through some of the most beautiful and most amazing land they had seen since Wisconsin. It was not long before they saw just how the river acquired its name. The water appeared to be a brownish, green. The name "Verdigris" was a French word that described the color of the river. As they rode to the south, they all marveled at the big rolling hills, wooded valleys, and seemingly abundant wildlife. Eagles and hawks flew overhead. Beaver scarcely noticed their presence. Deer only briefly gazed at them as they passed. Even a bobcat sat quietly between some bushes as the men rode by. This was truly God's country. Nevertheless, it was still too close to Niobrara, so they pushed southward.

That afternoon, they rode to the top of a tall hill east of the river. As they gazed over the breath-taking view, they noticed an unusual formation to their southeast. A large plateau seemed to lurch abruptly out of the ground. All edges were tall and steep, yet it was quite long and appeared to be completely flat on top. It appeared to be the tallest formation in miles. Perhaps from the top of this plateau they could spot an Indian camp. At the very least, they would be able to see a large part of the Verdigris River valley and locate possible sites for settlement. This demanded a closer inspection.

As they neared the unusual formation, they noticed rocks strewn about. The rocks were various sizes and shapes. At the northwest base, they looked up towards the top in amazement. The sides were steep and the top appeared to be nearly 150 feet above them. They rode around the base to the northeast side and found a spot where the slope to the top was not nearly as steep as those they had seen before.

"Well men," Samuel remarked. "This looks like as good a place as any to climb to the top." He dismounted, staked out his horse, and began the long climb to the top. The rest of the men followed him. Once to the top, they noticed the formation was completely flat, just as they had thought, with a few rocks scattered about the edges. The plateau was about 50 yards wide and 300 yards long. The men looked in all directions in awe. They could see for miles and miles in every direction. As they neared the southeastern most point, they all noticed that this side was neither as steep nor as tall as the other three sides. "Sure, we couldn't have kept right on ridin' until we reached this side, where we could've just walked right on up," Tite Sherman stated as he looked at Samuel. Everyone noticed a hint of sarcasm in his tone.

"Well, at least I didn't take you up the steepest part," Samuel replied as he noticed, rather sheepishly, that they could have even ridden their horses up on this side.

"C'mon, Dor and Sidney," William stated. "Let's go get the horses."

As Dor Carver, Sidney Haskin, and William Griffith went to bring the horses up, the rest of the men looked around at the breath-taking views. From this unusual plateau, which was formed more than a million years ago by glaciers, they could see the Verdigris River valley stretching for miles to the north and for miles to the south. The rolling hills to the south seemed to swallow the river. Samuel was gazing southward along the river when Titus Sherman came running toward him. "Samuel, Samuel," he said excitedly. "You've got to come see this."

Tite led Samuel and the others to the northwestern end of the plateau. There on the ground, he pointed to a large circle made of rocks, nearly 8 feet in diameter. Four lines of rocks radiated from the center. Samuel noticed that the four lines corresponded with the points on a compass. "We need to leave here, NOW!" he exclaimed.

As Samuel and the others quickly headed southeast along the plateau, they met Dor, Sidney, and William with the horses. "You men seem to be in somewhat of a hurry," Sidney noticed.

"We need to get away from this place," stated Samuel.

"What?" questioned Sidney

"I'll explain later," Samuel said as he and the others mounted their horses.

Samuel led the men back down the southeast side and then he turned his horse west toward the river. When he reached a clearing by the river, he stopped and turned toward the rest of the men who were looking at him rather puzzled.

"What the hell?" Samuel's brother questioned. By the tone of his voice, it was evident that he was slightly perturbed by his brother's actions. As the men were riding away from the plateau, Sidney had questioned Tite about what had caused their hasty retreat. All Tite knew was he had seen stones placed in a circle at the northwest end of the formation. Sidney had never seen his brother run from anything and now he seemed to be running from little stones on a hill.

"That plateau is a sacred place," Samuel explained, seemingly ignoring his brother's tone. "If we had been caught there, our chances for any friendly agreement with the Indians would have been greatly decreased."

"You men make camp here," Samuel continued. "Me and Wallis are going back to the plateau. Unless I miss my guess, we will soon be meeting the natives."

"But you just said that we shouldn't be caught there," began Griffith.

"We'll stay out of sight and if someone shows up, we will follow them to their camp," explained Samuel. "Take care of our horses. We'll go back on foot."

Father and son made their way back to the plateau. It was already late afternoon and both knew they may have to wait until the next day before anyone came to the strange circle of rocks. However, as they neared the tall, flat hill, they heard voices at the top. Samuel and Wallis quietly climbed to the top then ducked behind some bushes where they had a view of the entire plateau. To the northwest, and near the circle of rocks, they saw four Ponca men. All four were swaying side to side and chanting. When the chanting stopped, the oldest of the

Ponca began speaking in a language Samuel could not understand. The other three Indians listened as their elder spoke. Samuel guessed that the older man was a teacher and the other three were his students.

The Haskins watched with great interest. After an hour, the four Ponca braves walked across the plateau to the southeast, descended the hill, and headed south. Samuel and Wallis carefully followed at a safe distance so as not to be detected. For nearly an hour they followed the Indians south over hills and into valleys. Soon they approached a tall hill just east of a point where two branches of the Verdigris River met. At the top of the hill was a circle of 10 or 12 tepees. They had found the Indian camp.

It was almost dark when Samuel and Wallis returned to their own camp, which was four miles to the north of the Ponca encampment. John Brown was on guard and saw them coming. "Did you find the Indians?" he asked.

"They have a camp several miles south of here," Wallis replied.

"Tomorrow morning," said Samuel, "Me and Wall will take a pack horse of supplies as gifts to the Indians. Wallis, you and Dor go out first thing and get a couple deer."

The men had many questions, but Samuel insisted that they all turn in early and get a good night's sleep. By first light the next morning, Wallis and Dor had already left camp. Samuel prepared a packhorse with gifts of spices, salt, sugar, and blankets (all of which he had purchased while they were in Yankton). As Samuel finished packing the horse, Wallis and Dor returned with two deer freshly gutted and bound to a makeshift sled being pulled by their horse.

"Remain here until we return," directed Samuel. Then he and his son rode off with their gifts toward the Indian camp. This time, the Haskins made no attempt to hide themselves as they neared the Indian encampment. Both were singing and whistling in order to be heard as they approached. As they rode up to the base of the hill, two braves stepped out of the bushes and blocked their way.

Samuel took his pipe from his mouth and in a calm, low voice asked, "Do you speak English?"

"Yes," the one brave replied. "We speak white man tongue."

"We come as friends bearing gifts," stated Samuel. "May we enter your camp?"

The brave who had spoke to them nodded, then turned and walked back up the hill. Samuel and Wallis followed him as the other Ponca brought up the rear. The brave led them to the center of the camp. An older Ponca emerged from one of the tepees and looked at the strangers. "Who are these white-eyes that come into the village of Mon-e-ga-he, Arrow Chief of the Ponca?" he asked in the language of the white man.

"We are friends who come to honor Mon-e-ga-he," Samuel replied.

Wallis brought the packhorse in front of Arrow Chief, cut the sled loose, took the pack off the horse, and placed it on the sled with the deer. "Gifts for the great Mon-e-ga-he," he said.

Arrow Chief looked through the pack of supplies then looked up to the strangers. "White-eyes honor Arrow Chief," he said.

"Only one of us is white-eyes," Samuel stated. "My son's mother is Mohawk a tribe of the great Iroquois nation near the great water to the east."

Arrow Chief looked at Wallis. Then he turned to Samuel. "You join us for meal."

That afternoon Samuel and Arrow Chief talked. They spoke of many things. They spoke of the land, the animals, and the trees. They spoke of the white man running the Indian off his land. They spoke of the disease that white man had brought to the red man. Both spoke of simpler times of the past and they spoke of their dreams for the future. As his father spoke with the Chief, Wallis engaged in games of skill and strength with the braves. They shot targets with arrows, ran races, and wrestled. The braves were very impressed with the strength and speed that this young man possessed.

As evening neared, Arrow Chief said, "I will walk with you back to your camp."

Arrow Chief turned to his people, placed his hand on Samuel's shoulder, and said, "This is friend of Mon-e-ga-he. From this day forward, he shall be called Ke-ton-ga, the Great Turtle."

Then placing his hand on Wallis's shoulder, he told his people, "From this day the son of Ke-ton-ga shall be called Ke-zhin-ga, the Little Turtle."

As Arrow Chief and two of his braves walked down the hill toward the Verdigris River with Samuel and Wallis, Arrow Chief pointed to the land to the west and the south. "This would make good home for you," he stated.

Samuel looked at the grassy, rolling hills and the wooded valleys along the river. This was very pretty country, abundant in wildlife, and just far enough from the larger communities of Niobrara and Yankton that he could be very comfortable here. Yes, he did think that this would make a good home.

Samuel turned to his son and said, "Wall, ride to our camp and let the men know that we will be having guests for supper." Then, turning to Mon-e-ga-he, "You will be our guest for a feast tonight."

When they returned to Samuel's camp, Cyrus was preparing a feast of turkey and rabbit. Samuel introduced his new friends to his men. The men welcomed Mon-e-ga-he and his braves and the Arrow Chief told them he would help them find land.

After supper, Samuel stood up, placed his pipe in his mouth, and took a couple puffs. Then he told his men of the agreement he had made with Arrow Chief. "We will live in peace with the Ponca and the other tribes in the area," he began. "We will provide assistance to them when they are sick. We will not desecrate their burial grounds or their holy lands. We will not cut any trees and we will not trap any animals for fur. Instead, we will plant trees and we will care for the wildlife. We will hunt only what we can eat and we will not waste. We will bring the lumber for our homes from Yankton or mills along the Niobrara. We will live in harmony with the land and we will not abuse it. If we take care of the land, it will take care of us. If we do all these things, we have nothin' to fear from Mon-e-ga-he and his people."

"Tomorrow," Samuel continued, "Mon-e-ga-he and his people will help us locate lands for our homes. We will all go to Mon-e-ga-he's village in the morning."

Arrow Chief was pleased with his new friends. Just after dark, the three Ponca headed for their camp. Samuel watched them disappear into the woods as they headed south along the river. It had been a busy day and he knew that this was only the beginning. Shortly after the Ponca had left, all the men turned in for the evening. Early the next morning they broke camp and headed south for the Ponca village.

With the help of Mon-e-ga-he and his braves, six of the eight men staked out the corners of their claims. Samuel staked his claim along the river about a mile to the southwest of the hill where Arrow Chief's camp was located. Cyrus staked his claim just to the west of Samuel and along the creek south of Samuel. Wallis staked his along the river south of Samuel and Cyrus, while Dor located his in the hills to the northeast of Wallis. William located his claim just east of Samuel and along a small creek called the Cottonwood that ran to the south and west of Arrow Chief's camp. Tite found some land on the hills east of the river and about three miles southeast of Wallis for himself and his brother, Watts.

John Brown with the help of Shon-ge-ska, one of Arrow Chief's trusted braves decided to head back to the north and seek some land along the middle branch of the Verdigris River. He told Samuel that he would meet them at the land office in Niobrara in a few days. Everyone would be filing their claims at Niobrara before they started back to Wisconsin.

Samuel's brother, Sidney, did not see anything that he wanted along the Verdigris. Therefore, he and another trusted

Ponca brave of named Mon-ka-ta, headed to the southeast. They told Samuel that they would return in three or four days.

Samuel and Wallis took the opportunity to go hunting with their new Ponca friends. As they hunted, the Ponca showed them the rivers and streams in the area. After a couple days on the hunt, they returned to the Ponca village with some deer and antelope meat. That evening they enjoyed a feast and then sat around the campfire sharing stories and tall tales with Mon-e-ga-he's people.

The next evening, just before nightfall, Sidney and Mon-ka-ta rode into camp. Sydney had found some farmland about 15 miles to the southeast. It had been a long couple of days. Arrow Chief told all the men that they could stay and rest in his village as long as they needed. The men all slept late the next morning. Arrow Chief saw that they were not disturbed and the men stayed at the Indian village that day. During the day, Shon-ge-ska came walking in with news that John Brown had found some land along the Middle Branch and had gone to the land office in Niobrara. Now that everyone had located their claims, they would start back for Wisconsin the next day. Dor and Tite would go as far as Yankton and get some lumber and supplies, then return to the Verdigris River valley to start building homes on their claims while the other six men returned to Wisconsin.

Just before dark, Arrow Chief commented to Samuel that he did not think that Griffith looked well. Samuel agreed, but Griffith would not admit that anything was wrong. He was very pale and he was not acting like himself. Perhaps another good night's sleep would help him.

The morning rays of the sun glistened on the flowing waters of the Verdigris River One by one, Samuel and his men emerged from their teepees after a restful night of sleep in the Ponca camp. The Ponca women were preparing a farewell breakfast for the men. Everyone began packing his bedrolls. As Samuel finished saddling his horse, he noticed that William Griffith still was not awake. Samuel walked over to the teepee where William slept and called to him, but there was no response. Samuel entered the teepee and gently shook William to wake him, but still there was no response. As he turned William over, he noticed that William was dead.

That morning, the Ponca helped their new friends bury their companion. They placed William in a grave on the land to which he had just staked claim a couple days before. His final resting place was on a hillside overlooking the Cottonwood creek. As they laid him to rest, Samuel said a few words to honor his dear friend. The Ponca brought some wild flowers and some bushes and planted them around William's grave.

When the men returned to Mon-e-ga-he's camp, Samuel wrote a short note addressed to Annie telling her that they were on their way back and that William Griffith had died. Then he turned to Wallis handed him the note and said, "Ride ahead into Niobrara and mail this at once. Find John, let him know we are on our way. Tell him about William."

Wallis promptly mounted his horse and, without a word, he galloped off to the north. Samuel turned to Mon-e-ga-he, "My friend," he said, "you have honored us with your friendship. I ask that you look after Dor and Tite until I return."

"They are our brothers," Arrow Chief replied. "We will see no harm comes to them."

Samuel mounted his horse and waved to his Ponca friends and the five men rode off to the north.

The unusual plateau where the Haskins first
encountered the Ponca
Photo by D. R. Haskin.

Chapter 4   Goodbye Wisconsin

The evening air was exceptionally crisp, even for the middle of September in the village of LaValle. August Meyer was sweeping off the boardwalk in front of the general store. He stopped briefly to gaze up at the sky. "Yep," he said to himself, "it will freeze hard tonight." He was about to return to his sweeping as he glanced up the street and saw two men approaching on horseback. A second look revealed that those men were none other than Samuel and Wallis. "Ma," he shouted back into the store. "Ma, Wallis and Pa are back!"

Annie and Elizabeth stepped out onto the boardwalk just as Samuel and Wallis were dismounting. Samuel took his wife into his arms and looked over to his two adopted children. "I see you took good care of your mother while we was gone," he remarked. August and Elizabeth were full of questions about the trip, about the Indians, and about the new land. Samuel assured them he would tell them all about Nebraska, but first he needed to fill his belly. Wallis handed his bag to August and then took the horses to the stable.

That evening the men recounted their adventures to Annie and the children. Elizabeth drifted off to sleep about midnight, but August still had many questions. Samuel told the inquisitive youth that he would answer more questions in the morning. Feeling a little tired, August finally decided to head for bed. He picked up his nine-year-old sister, carried her to her room, and gently laid her in the soft feather bed. Then he covered her with a wool-spun blanket and quietly tiptoed to his own room where he crawled into bed thinking of the new lands in Nebraska. Within minutes, he was sound asleep.

The next morning, Samuel was up early. After he ate breakfast, he and Annie went over to the boarding house. Julia was just finishing dishes from the morning meal as Samuel and Annie arrived.

"May I get you anything?" Julia asked.

"No, thank you," Samuel answered. "How are you

49

doing?"

"Well, I've been doing a lot of thinking these past few weeks," she said. "With William gone and his children grown and now Media is to be married in a couple weeks, there is nothing for me here in Wisconsin."

Samuel looked over to Annie. "Media's getting' married?" he inquired.

"I forgot to mention it last night," replied Annie. "She's marryin' a preacher named A. J. Brill from up north."

"Do you think that I could make it in Nebraska?" asked Julia.

Samuel took his pipe out of his mouth and pondered her question for a few seconds. "I don't see why not," he said. "There is no reason you couldn't have a boarding house there. Annie, what do you think?"

"Sure," Annie replied. "We'll help you. And you will have other friends there too."

Julia decided she would go to Nebraska with the Haskins. She would open a boarding house there and she would prove up on the land to which her husband had filed claim. Now, there was much to do. Media would be married to the preacher man in a couple weeks. Julia would have to sell her boarding house. Sam and Annie would have to sell their store. They hoped that they would be ready to move in the spring. Samuel knew that his brother, Sidney, would not be ready until the following spring because he had some farming contracts he must fill this next year. He was not sure whether John and Charlotte Brown would be ready by spring. The Homestead Act provided them with five years to prove up on their claims, but Samuel was anxious to begin his new life in Nebraska.

As the spring of 1874 neared, Samuel knew that his plans for moving to Nebraska would have to be put on hold for one more year. His adopted son, August, was pledged to wed Andrew Jackson's daughter. Andrew owned some land just north of Baraboo and was giving it to the newly weds. The wedding was not going to be until October and Samuel knew that there was no chance of heading to Nebraska that late in the fall. When Cyrus Carver's boy, Shib, left in April, Samuel could only wish that he was going with him. Shib Carver would file claim to some land when he arrived and he was to help Dor build a cabin for their father. Cyrus and Mary were not going to move to Nebraska until their boys had their house finished.

In May, Tite Sherman's wife and daughter along with Watts Sherman and his family packed up and headed to their new home along the Verdigris Creek. Once again, Samuel yearned to go. Next year for sure, he and Annie would be packing their wagons with Julia Griffith and Wallis and they too would ride toward the sunset and to their new homes. Perhaps Cyrus' house would be finished by that time and they could go to Nebraska together. Samuel was pleased that Cyrus and Mary were still here. They had been close friends all their lives. Having Cyrus nearby was a comfort, even though Samuel was feeling more and more closed in as more and more people settled in the area around LaValle.

The fall of 1874 was one of the best on record for the farmers in the Baraboo hills of Wisconsin. Record crops meant more money to buy more goods and supplies from the merchants in the villages that lined the banks of the Baraboo River. Samuel, Annie, and Wallis were very busy in the store. Now it was just the three of them. August was married and he moved to a farm north of Baraboo with his wife and his little sister, Elizabeth. August had no plans to move to Nebraska now that he was married and he wanted his little sister with him. Samuel and Annie agreed that Elizabeth should be with her brother instead of with them in Nebraska.

The cold winter winds howled through the rolling hills of Sauk County. Samuel could not wait for the arrival of spring and the warmer temperatures. Winter was passing by much too slowly. How he longed to move to their new home, especially now that he had found a buyer for his store. Julia had already sold her boarding house and was now helping him and Annie with the mercantile. Nothing was going to stop them from moving this spring, or so he thought. However, in February, Wallis became pledged to wed Maria Sophia Brandt. She was the oldest child of Fred Brandt and Sophia Rabuck Brandt. The Brandts were a fine family and very close friends to the Haskins. Samuel had introduced Fred to Sophia many years before, and he was very pleased that their oldest daughter was going to marry his son. However, the Brandts requested that Maria Sophia wait until she turn seventeen before she married Wallis. They felt that sixteen was too young. Since her birthday was not until October 5th, Samuel was going to have to wait still another year before he could move to his new home.

Wallis tried to convince his parents to go on to Nebraska in the spring, and then he and Maria Sophia would follow the next spring. Nevertheless, Samuel was not about to miss his son's wedding. It was very hard for Samuel to watch his brother and the Browns leave for Nebraska that spring. Many of his friends had now left the Baraboo hills and he feared that by the time he got to Nebraska it would already be too crowded. No, he would just have to come to his senses. Shib and Dor Carver had been sending letters. According to them, the homesteaders still were not coming. Dor figured that between the fear of the Indians and the controversy over the railroad lands that it would be many years before large numbers of people came into the Verdigris River valley. He wrote that the Indians had not been any problem. They were honoring their agreement with Samuel and they were very helpful to the Carvers and the Shermans.

Dor also related in his letters that he saw the railroad land controversy as being a major blockade for future settlement of the area. In 1860, the United States had given the Burlington and Missouri River Railroad every odd numbered section of land within twenty miles of its main line. This meant that all the odd numbered sections of the Sherman Precinct in Antelope County belonged to the Burlington and Missouri. Both Tite Sherman and himself had filed claim on Railroad land, which in and of itself was not a problem. Burlington and Missouri would honor the title to the homestead if those who held the title made improvements to the property and maintained those improvements for five years. Burlington and Missouri, however, maintained the right to an easement should they decide to build a rail line through the property. Dor and Tite both knew those terms when they filed their claims. However, a Judge from Omaha had brought suit in the U.S. Court to recover those railroad lands, claiming that they had been obtained by fraud. If the court found in favor of this Judge, then Tite and Dor could lose their homesteads.

Samuel felt that he would have to look into that a little better, once he made it out there to Nebraska. Despite the seriousness of the controversy, he figured that it was helping to prevent a huge onslaught of settlers into his beautiful valley. He was also relieved that the Indians were honoring their agreement. He had wondered if his absence would create some problems. He was pleased to see the Indians were being helpful to Shib, Dor, Watts, Tite, and their families.

The spring of 1875 yielded to hot summer breezes in LaValle. Samuel kept busy in his store, because keeping himself busy was about the only way to stop thinking about Nebraska. Many evenings he and Annie would sit on the bench in front of the store and watch the sun set over the rolling hills. The yearning in his heart for Nebraska was growing stronger with each passing day. One evening, near the middle of July, the longing in his heart was so overpowering that he felt he was entire body was going to burst. He just had to get away for at least a little while. Perhaps a horseback ride along the Baraboo River would help.

Samuel told Annie that he was going for a ride, then he walked to the stable and saddled his horse. Mounting his horse, he rode south toward the woods near the banks of the Baraboo River. As he rode, he listened to the birds in the trees, allowing their songs to soothe his soul. The sound of the running river water also relaxed him. He pulled on the reins and stopped his horse. For several minutes, he just sat listening to the peaceful sounds as they poured into his soul from the hills, trees, and river. He felt immersed in joy and he saw himself at his homestead in Nebraska. He imagined being along the banks of the Verdigris.

Just then, another sound pierced sharply through the trees, silencing the birds and bringing Samuel back to reality. It was screaming. Someone was in trouble. Wasting no time, Samuel turned his horse in the direction of the screams and broke into a gallop. As he entered a clearing he saw Maria Sophia Brandt and her nine-year old sister Mary running frantically towards the trees to the left of the clearing. Behind them and closing fast, he saw a she-bear. Then he noticed a bear cub between the girls and the oncoming mother. The mother passed her cub and continued her charge toward the frightened girls. Samuel guessed just what had happened. The girls must have been playing with the bear cub when its mama came on the scene. Everyone knows that mother bears are not to be reckoned with when it comes to protecting their cubs.

Samuel saw that Maria Sophia and Mary would never make it to the trees in time. He tried to goad his horse into moving toward the bears, but the horse was not about to move in that direction. So, Samuel grabbed his rifle and jumped off the horse. As he did, the horse turned and galloped back the way they had come. No time to think about it, Samuel shot into the air. He did not want to kill the bear unless he absolutely had to. Still, the bear continued its charge at the fleeing girls. Samuel shouted to the bear and fired another shot into the air. The noise must have been too much for the cub, which began to cry and run in a direction away from Samuel, away from the girls, and most importantly, away from its mother. Hearing the cub's cries, the mother stopped and looked back toward her baby. Noticing that it was running in the opposite direction, she turned and ran after it.

Samuel breathed a heavy sigh of relief. He knew that if he had been forced to shoot again, he would have had to shoot to kill. He looked back for his horse, but it was long gone. Then, he looked back to the clearing and saw the girls were running toward him. "You both all right?" he asked as they ran up to him.

Both were out of breath and Mary had tears rolling down her cheeks. Samuel reached down and picked her up. "It's fine now," he said. "Let's get you girls home."

As he walked the girls to their cabin, Mary told Samuel how they had found the bear cub and thinking that it was cute, they started petting it. Then for some reason it made a noise and before they knew it, the mother came out of the woods and was charging at them. Samuel told they girls that bear cubs are not pets and that if they see one, its mother is not far away. The girls both nodded their heads.

Mary did most of the talking as they walked back to the Brandt cabin. She was a talkative little girl. Her older sister, on the other hand, was very shy. Even now, she had not said one word to Samuel. But, who could get a word in with Mary jabbering away like she was. As they came within sight of the cabin, Maria Sophia nervously and with a great deal of hesitation asked Samuel, "Do we have to tell Father?"

Samuel looked down at her and smiled. She had tears in her eyes and he could tell she was genuinely frightened. "Don't you think we better?" he asked.

"He'll whoop us, sure," she replied rather shyly.

Samuel knew that Fred Brandt was strict with his children and had heard that his punishment could be excessive. "I'll talk to him," Samuel explained. "It will be fine."

Samuel could tell that Maria Sophia did not seem very relieved, but she replied, "Thank you, Mr. Haskin."

Samuel explained to Fred what had happened and told him that he thought both girls had learned their lesson and the main thing was that they were both all right. He assured Fred that no one was hurt and no harm had been done. Fred thanked him and then looked at both girls, "You know better." Both girls lowered their heads.

"Don't punish them for this, Fred," Samuel requested of his friend. "They have punished themselves plenty by the way they are feeling."

"You right," he said in his heavy German accent.

As Samuel walked home, he hoped that Fred was just going to let it drop. He knew that both girls would laugh about the incident some day. He figured it would sure be a good story for their kids. Then he said to himself, "Maria Sophia's kids. They'll be my grandkids. Ha, what a story." In just a few months, Maria Sophia would be married to Wallis. He knew that she would make Wallis a good wife, but he worried how she would handle moving to the un-tamed lands of Nebraska. She would be so far from the only home she has ever known and her parents were not planning to move out there for several more years, if they planned to move at all. It would be very hard for her. She was just a girl and she was very shy. Nevertheless, Samuel admired her because he knew that even though she was very frightened by the prospect of moving to Nebraska, she still planned on going. That was the mark of true bravery and he admired that. He and Annie would do everything they could to see no harm came to her.

When Samuel returned to the stable, he saw his horse was there standing by the door. He was not surprised to find it there. He figured that when he jumped off to rescue the girls, the horse would run right back to its stall. He caught the horse, removed its bridle and saddle, and then brushed it down. The poor animal was still nervous from its experience. A little grain and some hay calmed it right down. Well, so much for that peaceful ride along the banks of the Baraboo. Samuel put the horse in its stall and headed home.

As he strolled down the dusty street, he once again imagined himself along the banks of the Verdigris River. He imagined himself sitting in the camp of Mon-e-ga-he, the Arrow Chief of the Ponca. In his vision, they were throwing a feast for him and Annie. He could almost taste the tender venison and could almost smell the smoke from the campfire. And, was that the flowing waters of the Verdigris he heard, as it ran on its never-ending journey, carving its way northward through the rolling hills of his new home? How he longed to be there now. Could he endure yet another winter here in Wisconsin? So many settlers were moving into the area these days. LaValle was no longer a small settlement, no longer a tiny village. It was becoming a bustling city. A city was no place for Samuel Haskin. The call of the west was growing louder and louder in his heart and echoed through his very soul.

Toward the middle of September, Sam and Annie received a letter from Elizabeth Dalrymple. She lived at Neligh with her son, Charles, and she kept busy making and mending clothes. She said that while the Indian raids in the area had not stopped completely, they were not as frequent or as intense as they had been just a couple years earlier. However, the reports were that the Indians were still making a nuisance of themselves in the more remote parts of the county and had been chasing would-be settlers away from the creek and river valleys.

Elizabeth stated that there had been some nasty raids to the west of Neligh. The Indians had forced their way into a house of some woman who was home alone with her young baby and brother-in-law. The Indians demanded food and drink, then took to helping themselves. The poor woman tried to get her brother-in-law to go to a neighbor's place for help, but he was too frightened to do so. Since she could not get him to go for help, she grabbed a bucket and acted as if she was going out to get some water. Once she was out of the cabin, she dropped the bucket and began to run for the neighbor's place. When she was about half way, she heard a noise behind her and could see two of the Indians coming after her. She knew that she could not out-run them so she stopped. They grabbed her and told her she had to go back or they would kill her baby. The Indians stayed at her place until about midnight eating and drinking.

Elizabeth went on to say that the next day the same Indians went up to the house of one of the woman's neighbors. They began to fire shots into the house and then killed some chickens and a cow. Afterwards, they stood outside the house for several minutes yelling and laughing before they moved off toward the Elkhorn River. Later that night, they returned and stole some horses.

After reading Dalrymple's letter, Samuel wondered if Cyrus had heard anything from his boys. It was a good day for a buggy ride, so he hitched his team and he and Annie rode out to the Carver place. As they pulled up to the house, they saw nine-year-old Donaley sitting on the step. "Your Pa 'round?" Samuel asked.

"Pa, the Haskins be here." He shouted back into the house.

Cyrus stepped out of the house and walked over to the buggy. "Come on in fer a spell," he stated.

"We're just out for a little ride," Samuel said declining his friend's offer.   "I brought you a letter we got from Dalrymple. Have you heard from your boys?"

"Just a couple weeks ago," Cyrus replied. "They be doin' good, but doesn't sound like they will have my house ready by spring."

"Dalrymple says there's still some Indian trouble near the rivers and creeks," Samuel remarked as he handed the Dalrymple letter to Cyrus. "Your boys say anything?"

"They said that there was word the Sioux were heading their way," Cyrus answered. "But, Mon-e-ga-he's people kind of talked them out of it. Guess it took a little exchange of arrows though."

Samuel was relieved. He sure wished he were there, however. He worried about Shib and Dor and he worried about the Shermans. He felt that if he were only there, he would be able to work some bargain with the Sioux. But, it sounded like Mon-e-ga-he was taking very good care of the Carvers and the Shermans. Still, Samuel knew that he should be there to help. He felt responsible for their safety. After all, those men were there only because he had assured them that the Indians would not give them any trouble. He knew that the Ponca would not bother them, but he had not had a chance to talk to the Sioux. Obviously, the Ponca were going to do all they could to protect his people, but he still needed to be there. Yes, he needed to be there. He made up his mind that nothing was going to keep him from moving the next spring. Nothing!

By the first part of October, the farmers were well into the fall harvest. There was going to be another good crop this year, which would mean plenty of food and supplies to last the winter. It also meant that the general store would be very busy once again. That pleased Samuel because he knew that it would make the Wisconsin winter pass more quickly.

On October 10th, Wallis married Maria Sophia Brandt. Most of the family was there. August, his wife, and his sister, Elizabeth, came from Baraboo. Nancy Ann and her family came too. Edwin Haskin was able to get some time off from his mail route so he and his family were able to attend. Cyrus Carver hosted the wedding dance. Fiddle players, a couple of accordions, and even a jug player made for a fantastic hoedown. You could always count on the Carvers to throw a great dance.

A couple of weeks after the wedding, Frederick Rabuck came running in to the mercantile. His oldest daughter, Delphine, was gone. He wondered if Samuel and Annie had seen or spoken with her. Samuel told him that they had not seen her and asked Frederick what had happened. Frederick told him that his wife and Del were not getting along and that his wife's daughter, Elizabeth Ann, fought with Del a couple days before. Del had left a letter telling her father that she was leaving and never coming back.

Samuel was worried. Delphine was only fifteen years old and he knew that she had taken her mother's death very hard. Samuel tried to reassure Frederick that everything would be fine, but he was not so sure himself. When he had spoke with Del a couple weeks before, she had complained to him that her father's new wife, Mary, was not her mother and would never be her mother. Samuel knew that Del felt as if Mary was trying to replace her mother. It was difficult for Samuel too. Therefore, he understood how confused Del had to be.

A couple weeks later, Frederick received a letter from his

daughter. She was in Iowa and had found a job cleaning house for an elderly couple. She said that she was fine and that she missed her father and her brothers and sisters. Frederick showed the letter to Samuel and Annie. Once again, Samuel tried to assure Frederick that Del was going to be fine. Even though Samuel, himself, was very worried about her, he had to keep a positive outlook.

Wallis and his new bride rented a small cabin on the edge of LaValle, near the Fred Brandt home, so Maria Sophia could help her mother during the day. A couple days a week, Wallis would help at the stable and, on the other days, he helped his parents at the mercantile. In February, Maria Sophia learned that she was pregnant. Samuel was pleased for Wallis and his wife.

With Wallis married, Samuel once again began making plans for the move to Nebraska in the spring. He was planning to leave Wisconsin at the end of April because the sooner they made the trip, the easier it would be on Maria Sophia. However, a late winter storm hit the area during the middle of the month and Samuel had to postpone the trip until May. Then, with the melting and spring rains, he decided to wait until the end of May. By the time May finally arrived, there was much to do. The sale of the mercantile was finalized, they sold their house, and sold many of their personal items. Three wagons were prepared for the journey and packed with supplies, household items, and personal effects.

On May 29th, Samuel, Annie, Julia Griffith, Wallis and Maria Sophia were packed and the wagons loaded. Maria Sophia was now five months pregnant and Samuel worried how she would handle the trip that lie ahead of them. Before they left LaValle, they stopped by the Carver place. Samuel had hoped that Cyrus and his family could go with them, but Shib had sent a letter telling his parents that their house would not be ready for them until late in the fall. Cyrus told Samuel that he would move his family the next spring. After wishing his good friends a safe journey, Cyrus, Mary and their kids watched as Samuel's three wagons rolled down the muddy street toward the edge of

LaValle.

At the west side of LaValle, they stopped at the Brandt cabin. Maria Sophia's parents and her brothers and sisters were standing in front waiting for them. Wallis helped his wife down from the wagon and her brothers and sisters gathered around her. Ten-year old Mary was crying. Maria Sophia and Mary had always been very close. Fred and Sophia worked their way through the huddle of children to bid their daughter farewell. Sophia smiled and took her oldest daughter into her arms. "My baby is all grown now," remarked Sophia with great pride. "Make sure to write us when you get there, and write us when the baby comes."

Maria Sophia nodded then turned to her father. However, from him there were no good byes, no hugs. He had never been one for tenderness or emotion. "Do as Wallis says," he stated and then turned to Samuel. "Let me know how it goes out there. If the land is ripe and folks can still stake claim, I may come in a year or two."

Maria Sophia showed a little surprise at that statement. Her father had never mentioned leaving Wisconsin. Nevertheless, she did not have time to think about that now. They needed to get on their way. Wallis helped her back into the wagon and as they pulled away, Maria Sophia's brother Charley, who had just turned twelve years old, shouted, "Send me one of them Indian arrows." He had heard Samuel and Wallis talking about the Indian camp and at his age things like that fascinated him.

Samuel had one more stop to make before they could leave LaValle forever. On their way out of town, they pulled up to the gates of a small cemetery. Samuel walked over to one of the graves while Annie and the others stayed with the wagons. He took off his hat and with a tear rolling down his cheek he kneeled down and gently placed his hand on the headstone. Then, his voice cracking, he said, "My dearest daughter, leaving you here is the hardest thing I've ever had to do. I wish you could go with us. You would love Nebraska. We have a new home there. It is near a river and there are rolling hills and woodlands. Raviah, my dear Raviah, I will never forget you."

Suddenly, he could almost feel Raviah's loving hand on his shoulder. It was as if she was telling him that she was there with him and would always be with him. He felt at peace. For the first time since her death, he finally felt at peace. With tears in his eyes, Samuel raised his big, robust body, placed his hat on his head, then turned and walked toward the wagons. He crawled up into the wagon then looked at Annie and smiled reassuringly. As they slowly pulled away, Annie placed her hand on Samuel's arm and then looked back towards the cemetery, back towards the place where her daughter lay in eternal rest. With tears rolling down her cheeks, she whispered, "Good bye."

Chapter 5   Settling In

The Haskins and Julia Griffith followed the same path that Samuel and his scouts had traveled three years earlier. Slowly and patiently, the three wagons rolled across northern Iowa and through the southeastern part of Dakota. During the day, they pushed on as fast as they could. At night, they made their beds under their wagons. After 37 days on the trail, they pulled into the city of Yankton on the Missouri River. Samuel and Wallis purchased some supplies and a couple wagonloads of timber. Samuel arranged for the timber to be delivered to them by the first of the next week. Then on the 38th day after they left LaValle, they found themselves on a ferryboat crossing the Missouri River into Nebraska. As they rolled the wagons off the ferry onto the sandy Nebraska soil, Samuel took a deep breath. The smell of the wild Nebraska winds made him feel 20 years younger. They would stay in Niobrara for the night, and in one more day, he would finally be home.

The next morning the three wagons rolled south following the Verdigris River. By mid-afternoon on July 7th 1876, the wagons pulled up to the Haskin and Griffith homesteads. As Samuel and Julia stopped their wagons, Wallis pulled up beside them. "Me and Maria Sophia are heading on to our place," Wallis told Samuel. Wallis was anxious to show his homestead to his new wife. Samuel nodded and Wallis drove his wagon on to the south. Samuel admired his son's wife. She was now heavy with child and Samuel knew that the trip had not been easy for her. Still, she had not complained.

Samuel's group had not gone un-noticed as they pulled up to their new home. Samuel was helping Annie down from the wagon when Julia screamed. Looking up, Samuel followed Julia's gaze to the east and saw Arrow Chief and two of his braves approaching the wagons. Annie walked over to Julia and put her hand on Julia's shoulder. "It's alright, dear," Annie reassured her. "They won't harm us."

Samuel walked over to Arrow Chief.   "My friend,"

Samuel said. "It is great to see you again."

Mon-e-ga-he was pleased that Samuel had remembered his friend. He smiled at Samuel and said, "It has been long time." Then he looked toward the women.

Annie walked toward him. "I am wife of Ke-ton-ga," she said referring to Samuel by the name the Ponca had given him three years before. "I am honored to meet the mighty Mon-e-ga-he of the Ponca." Then turning toward Julia, who was still unsure of the whole situation, Annie stated, "This is our good friend Julia. She is wife of William who you met three years ago."

"William's wife be welcome here," Arrow Chief stated.

As Annie was introducing Julia to Mon-e-ga-he, Samuel grabbed a package of jerky, sugar, salt, and spices from his wagon. He walked back over to Arrow Chief and offered him the package. "For my good friend and his people," said Samuel. "Would you join us for our evening meal?"

"You once again honor Mon-e-ga-he," Arrow Chief remarked. "We will join you."

As Annie prepared the evening meal, Samuel and Julia took one of the wagons and surveyed the Griffith homestead. Julia seemed pleased with her new land, but she knew that it was going to be a daunting task to turn it into a home. Samuel assured her that he and Annie would help her and that she could live with them until they were able to build her house. After surveying the homestead, he took Julia to William's grave. Samuel remained at the wagon as Julia paid her respects. When she returned to the wagon, she said, "Yes, I will make it here. I have to, for him." Then she fell into Samuel's arms and sobbed uncontrollably.

That evening Samuel, Annie, and Julia had a feast with Mon-e-ga-he and his two braves. Maria Sophia was exhausted from her long trip from Wisconsin, so she and Wallis stayed at their own homestead. Samuel enjoyed talking to his Ponca friends. All evening they spoke of their culture and of hunting and fishing. They asked about Annie's people and about their ways and customs. Mon-e-ga-he gave Annie the Ponca name Mi-ta-in which means crescent moon. Shortly before midnight, Arrow Chief and his braves bid Samuel, Annie and Julia good-bye and made their way back to their camp.

There was much to do over the next few days for Samuel and Wallis. The Carvers and the Shermans came to offer their assistance. On the Wallis Haskin homestead, Wallis and the Shermans dug a hole into a hill overlooking the River. They leveled off the bottom, the sides, and the back. They hewed out the sod, which they had removed from the hole, into rectangular blocks and stacked those at the front. When the wagonloads of timber arrived, they framed a door at the front and fashioned a frame for the roof. Then, they covered the roof with sod and grass. Wallis made a door from some lumber he had brought with him from Wisconsin. After eight days of hard work, Wallis and Maria Sophia had a one-room sod house, measuring 12 feet by 16 feet It wasn't very big, but it would serve as temporary shelter for them until something more permanent was completed. Wallis then began to work on a log cabin at the northwest end of his homestead.

On the Samuel Haskin homestead, Samuel and the Carver boys set about preparing a dug-out into a hillside at the northeast side of Samuel's homestead near the Antelope and Knox county line. They dug a large, rounded hole at the top edge of the hill. The back part of the hole was eight feet deep and because of the slope of the hill, the front was level with the ground. Samuel then built the front from the timber that had arrived from Yankton. There was a door in the front with two windows, one on each side of the door. The top was made of timbers and wood. After nearly two weeks of painstaking work, Samuel and Annie had a log-fronted dugout that measured 28 feet by 24 feet. The inside was partitioned into three rooms – a bedroom for Samuel and Annie, a bedroom for Julia, and the main room. From the front of their new home, they had a spectacular view of the Verdigris River valley to the west.

When the dugout was finished, Annie and Julia moved

their personal belongings in while Samuel and Dor Carver began work on a stable for the horses. They placed the stable nearly 50 yards north of the dug-out and next to the county line at the north end of the homestead. Samuel and Dor dug two holes into the hillside and fashioned the roof out of logs, twigs, tree bark, and straw. When it was finished, the stable had two stalls, each capable of housing two horses.

Samuel's next task was to help Wallis build his log cabin. It was already the middle of August and Samuel knew Maria Sophia would soon have her baby. He knew that Wallis wanted to have the cabin completed by the time the baby was born. Wallis had already leveled off the land and had laid the first couple rows of logs. Samuel hoped that with his help, Wallis would be able to have the cabin complete by the middle of September. However, the first part of September brought several days of heavy rains that delayed construction.

By the last week of September, the cabin was nearly finished. Just one more week and the cabin would be ready. Maria Sophia's baby, however, did not want to wait for the finished product. Early in the morning on September 27th, Maria Sophia went into labor. Wallis rode to his parents place to get his mother. As Samuel hitched the wagon, Wallis rode back to his sod house. Annie arrived just minutes before the baby made its appearance. Annie had helped many mothers deliver their babies in Wisconsin. She knew just what to do and gently reassured Maria Sophia as she delivered her first-born. The little one, a girl, was not much bigger than seven pounds. Annie cut the umbilical chord and gingerly cleaned the baby with a damp towel. Annie then handed the little girl back to its mother. Wallis and Maria Sophia named the little girl Mercedes Adelia. She was a healthy baby with dark hair on the top of her head.

Within a week after Mercedes was born, the log cabin was finally completed. Maria Sophia had regained her strength and the baby was doing well. The young Haskin family moved all their belongings from the soddy to the new cabin. Samuel and Annie, Julia, the Carvers, and the Shermans had supper with them in their new cabin on their first night. Baby Mercedes was the highlight of the evening and everyone took turns holding her. A few days later, John and Charlotte Brown came to see the baby. Mercedes was the first white girl child born in the area.

The Haskins and Julia spent that winter settling into their new homes. Samuel and Wallis went on several hunting trips with Mon-e-ga-he's people. They also made a couple trips into Niobrara during the winter to post some letters to Wisconsin. While Wallis was away, Maria Sophia stayed with Annie and Julia. She still had not met any of the Ponca, even though their camp was only a mile or so from her cabin. Wallis had offered to take her to the Ponca camp on different occasions, but she had never been around Indians and was nervous. She knew that there were Indian tribes in Wisconsin, but to her knowledge, they were nowhere near LaValle. She was not used to having an Indian camp so close. Wallis was understanding and he didn't push it. He knew that in time she would become accustomed to living together with the Ponca.

As spring came, the Haskins planted cottonwood trees and plowed ground to grow crops. Samuel was anxious to start on Julia's house and Wallis needed some lumber for a barn. On April 4th, 1877, Samuel and Wallis hitched up their wagons to make a trip to Yankton for some seeds, lumber, and supplies. Wallis asked Maria Sophia if she wanted to stay at his parents' place while he was gone, but she said that she would stay at the cabin. He was a little surprised with her decision to stay alone. She had become a little more comfortable over the past couple months and she felt she would be all right alone. Besides, Annie agreed to check on her every day.

Samuel figured that they would be back in about a week. Before they began their trip to Yankton, they stopped at the Ponca camp. Samuel told Arrow Chief that they were going to be gone for several days to get supplies from the Missouri River. Samuel asked Mon-e-ga-he if he would keep an eye on their women while he and Wallis were away. Arrow Chief was honored and he told Samuel and Wallis that he would see that no harm would come to the women.

Maria Sophia woke up early on April 7th. Mercedes had been fussy all night and was still restless. Even after Maria Sophia fed her, the baby was still uneasy. It was a warm and sunny morning and Maria Sophia figured that it would be a good day to do laundry. She laid Mercedes in her cradle and placed it on the south side of the cabin so the baby could enjoy the warmth of the gentle spring breezes. Maria Sophia gazed to the south over the Verdigris River. She could hear the robins singing in the trees and hoped that their relaxing chorus would calm her daughter. She filled her washtub on the west side of the cabin and placed a cake of lye soap into the tub.

Mercedes continued to cry as her mother rubbed clothes over the washboard. Maria Sophia then rinsed the clothes and began hanging them to dry. Just then, she noticed that Mercedes had abruptly stopped her crying. She ran over to the south side of the cabin and as she came around the corner, she screamed. Mercedes was no longer in her cradle. Instead, she was being held in the arms of an Indian. Maria Sophia fought her fear and ran towards her baby.

She did not know it, but the Indian was Shon-ge-ska, White Wolf of the Ponca and a close friend of Wallis. He had been walking past the cabin to make sure that all was well when he heard the baby crying. Thinking that there may be trouble, he had come to investigate. When he saw the baby crying and did not see Maria Sophia, he thought the baby was frightened so he picked her up and began rocking her in his arms. Just then, Maria Sophia had come around the corner of the cabin and screamed.

As Maria Sophia ran towards White Wolf, he could see that she was very frightened. This was the first time that he had seen the wife of Ke-zhin-ga. She certainly was not what he expected. In his mind Wallis's wife was a strong woman, very brave, a wife fit for a great warrior. However, what he saw was a very young and very frightened girl. He knew that this land would certainly strengthen her in time. As he handed Mercedes to Maria Sophia he said, "Ta-in-ge," which was Ponca for Coming Moon. This would be Maria Sophia's Ponca name, however, Maria Sophia did not understand what he said. As White Wolf turned and walked toward the river, Maria Sophia found that she was too frightened to move.

For what seemed like an eternity, she stood there holding her baby and shaking like a leaf in a heavy wind. That was the closest she had ever been to an Indian, except for her mother-in-law, who was only half-Indian. Finally, she summoned up the courage to move. Without finishing the laundry and without looking back, she walked the ¾ mile north to Samuel and Annie's place.

Annie was also hanging up clothes to dry when she looked up and saw Maria Sophia coming quickly over the south hill. She could tell that something was wrong so she went to meet her. Maria Sophia ran up to Annie sobbing. "What's wrong dear child?" Annie asked fearing that something was wrong with the baby.

Maria Sophia was out of breath and was unable to speak. Annie took the baby from her daughter-in-law and saw that Mercedes was fine. With Mercedes in one arm, she took Maria Sophia by the hand and led her to the dugout. Maria Sophia set down once they were inside and Julia gave her a drink of water. Once again Annie asked, "What is it dear child? The baby is fine. Did something happen?"

Maria Sophia told Annie and Julia what had happened. Annie smiled. "My dear little child," Annie reassured, "he wasn't going to hurt you or your baby."

"How can you be sure?" Maria Sophia asked.

"Sweetie, they are only making sure we are all right. They promised Sam and Wal that they would watch out for us."

Despite Annie's reassurance, Maria Sophia was still frightened. Annie knew that it was very difficult for her. She was so young and so far away from her family and the home she had known all of her life. By late afternoon, Maria Sophia had calmed down, but she still did not want to go back to her cabin.

She asked Annie if she could stay there until the men returned. "Why, of course you can, little one," Annie replied.

As Samuel and Wallis returned on April 10th, they stopped at the Ponca camp to give them some supplies. Shonge-ska told Wallis what had happened. White Wolf feared that if he frightened Ta-in-ge, his name for Maria Sophia, that Ke-zhinga would be angry with him. Wallis assured him that everything was fine and that he would speak with Maria Sophia. White Wolf and the rest of the Ponca had a great respect for both Wallis and Samuel and would never do anything to cause them or their families harm. They were pleased that Wallis was understanding in this matter.

Wallis found his wife and baby, Mercedes, at his parent's place. During their ride to their own cabin, Wallis told her that his friend Shon-ge-ska was only checking on her and the baby to make certain that they were safe. Maria Sophia still was not so sure. How she wished that she could be brave about this. She knew that the Indians were friends with Wallis and perhaps in time she would come to accept that.

That spring, Samuel and Wallis planted corn, sorghum, and potatoes. They also plowed ground and planted some crops for Julia. After planting the crops, Samuel began work on Julia's cabin. She had decided upon a spot that overlooked the creek, which was about 300 yards south and a little east of Samuel and Annie's dugout. Samuel dug a large basement into the hillside and then began laying the logs for the cabin. The Carver's had finished the cabin for their parents and began helping Samuel with Julia's cabin.

Cyrus and Mary Carver arrived with their children on July 1st and Samuel was thrilled to see his old friend again. Cyrus' cabin set down the creek south of Samuel's dugout about ¾ of a mile. It was within a quarter of a mile north and west of Wallis and Maria Sophia's cabin. On July 4th, Cyrus held a dance, just like the old days in Wisconsin. Cyrus knew how to throw a good party. The Haskins, the Shermans, and the Browns from the Middle Branch area all enjoyed the music, dancing, and fun.

Samuel felt so alive here in Nebraska. Most of his close friends were here, but he missed his son, Edwin, as well as the Brandts and the Rabucks. In the letters he received from the Brandts, they wrote that they were anxious to see Maria Sophia's baby, however, Sophia was now with child and Fred really did not want to leave Wisconsin. Maria Sophia was expecting the arrival of her second baby in December and Samuel hoped that would tempt the Brandts to move west.

Frederick Rabuck explained in his letters that his family was doing fine. He wrote that he had given some thought to leaving Wisconsin, but did not want to leave his brother and sister. While the thought of moving west appealed to him, he felt he must stay in Wisconsin, at least for a few more years.

Samuel also received regular letters from his son, Edwin, who worked for the government carrying mail. Edwin's mail contract would be up by the end of the year and he was planning to bring his family to Nebraska the next spring. His wife, Delia, was just as anxious to head west because her brothers, the Shermans, were already in Nebraska.

By the end of the summer, Julia's cabin was finished. It was a large cabin with a kitchen area, living area, and four small bedrooms. Julia planned to open a boarding house here, just as she had done in Wisconsin. She hoped that there would be hired farmhands, housekeepers, teachers, or even travelers who would require housing. Samuel and Annie helped Julia move her personal belongings into her new home.

During the second week of September, Samuel and Annie were surprised when a wagon pulled up in front of their dugout and a man helped a young girl onto the ground. The man then took a couple bags off the wagon and placed on the ground then drove on. At first, the Haskins did not recognize the young girl with dark hair, but as she walked toward the door of the dugout, they saw it was none other than Delphine Rabuck. The Haskins were very pleased to see their oldest grandchild. Del told them that she missed being with family, but did not want to go back to her father because she did not like her father's wife, Mary. Moreover, she absolutely despised Mary's daughter Elizabeth Ann.

"Grandfather," Del asked, "would it be possible for me to stay here?"

Annie did not give Samuel a chance to answer. "Why of course you can stay here," she said. "Julia Griffith just moved out and you can stay in her room."

Samuel was very pleased that Del had come back to her family. She seemed more mature now than the last time he had seen her. Del told them that she had wrote a note to her father to let him know that she would be coming to Nebraska. She left Iowa with some friends, who came as far as Yankton. From there she caught a ride to Niobrara. When she asked about the Haskin's in Niobrara, a young man by the name of Elroy Crum, who lived west of a new settlement called Creighton, knew exactly where Samuel lived and offered to give her a ride.

That evening, Wallis, Maria Sophia, and Mercedes came for supper. Del just could not believe that Maria Sophia was a mother now and that Mercedes was so big. The last time she had seen Wallis and Maria Sophia was at their wedding. Del spent the evening talking with her family and learning about their lives in the Verdigris River valley.

Autumn's harvest was a good one for the settlers along the banks of the Verdigris. There would be plenty of food for the winter. Sorghum was made into molasses and corn was ground into meal. Root cellars had been dug for potatoes and for other foods to be stored during the winter ahead. A portion of the harvest had been kept as seeds for planting in the spring. There was no waste. The cane stocks and the corncobs would be used for cooking fires and heat for the winter. Earlier in the fall, the prairie grasses were cut and stacked for hay.

During the second week of November, Samuel went into Creighton for some supplies and any mail. Once a month, someone from the area would make the supply run. When they first arrived in the valley, they would get their mail and supplies from Niobrara. However, Creighton was much closer and had grown considerably over the past few months. Samuel, therefore arranged for all their mail to be delivered to there, instead. Besides, the settlers of the area could now purchase many of their supplies at Creighton. Lumber, however, still had to be purchased from Niobrara or even Yankton. If they could only have a post office right here in the valley, it would make life a lot easier for everyone. Perhaps when Edwin arrived, he could help secure a post office for the valley. Edwin had delivered mail in Wisconsin since his discharge from the Union army.

Samuel delivered everyone's mail and supplies as he returned from Creighton. Several letters had come from family and friends who were still in Wisconsin. He and Annie had received a letter from Edwin. He was pleased to hear that Edwin had made all the arrangements to move to Nebraska in the spring. Wallis and Maria Sophia had received a letter from the Brandts. Sophia had a baby on October 1st. It was a little boy that they had named Edward. However, Fred gave no indication as to if, or when, they would come out to Nebraska.

Winters in northeast Nebraska could be extreme. This year, the season began with a fierce snowstorm at the end of November and the snow and cold continued throughout the month of December. On the day before Christmas, Maria Sophia gave birth to another little girl. This time, Mary Carver braved the elements to help deliver the baby. Mary lived only a quarter of a mile from the younger Haskin and besides Mary was very experienced at such matters. Many times, in Wisconsin, the neighbors would call upon her to help with many of their medical needs. Wallis and Maria Sophia named their baby Florence Augusta. Florence was bigger than Mercedes had been at birth and had many of her father's characteristics. She had her father's eyes and nose. Mercedes, who was now over a year old, was not quite sure what to think of the new baby. She had always been the center of attention, but now it seemed that Florence held that honor.

The new baby made the Christmas of 1877 very special

for the Haskins. Annie fixed the Christmas dinner and she, Samuel, and Del spent the day with Wallis and Maria Sophia. Annie had made a little doll for Mercedes, which she played with all day and fell asleep while still holding onto the doll that night. The year of 1877 had been a good one for the settlers of the valley. Samuel could think of no better way to end the year than with the birth of a new granddaughter. Florence was a special Christmas gift and Samuel knew that she would continue to give her family joy for many more Christmases to come.

Chapter 6   Jessup

"It was April, 1878, Edwin Haskin loaded his family into a covered wagon heavily loaded and drawn by two old horses, left the woodland hills of Wisconsin and started on his long journey to Nebraska. Grandfather and Uncle had proceeded him two years before. There were five of us children, baby Cora Haskin Buxton but two months old. It was a wet, cold spring. Many perhaps will remember the snow and wind in those days. I remember it was out of one mud hole into another.

"In Iowa, father bought another horse, then we got on better. It was fun for us children, only when we camped at night, I being the oldest girl had to hold the baby while mother cooked supper on a camp fire, often in the rain and prepare beds for the night. We arrived at our destination May 21. Father took a homestead 12 miles west of Creighton. Then began the heart breaking task of building up a new home. The lumber for the house was hauled from the saw mills on the Niobrara river for father insisted on building a frame house, the first in the precinct. The goods he had shipped from Wisconsin had to be hauled from Yankton, South Dakota, it taking 4 days to make that trip. Then there had to be a school house built and logs had to be hauled from the Niobrara river.

"Our house was but a wall shanty that first summer. And how I remember those awful rains and wind storms. Father was gone from home so much. The roof was almost no shelter and frail little mother would gather her brood around her and wonder if we would be blown away. Our first term of school was taught by a Miss Viola Burton. Later Mrs. Will Sherman. We had but three month terms. Brother Spencer and I walked about two and a half miles and were often caught in blizzards. I being the only girl in the bunch of boys that came our way, was put between two large boys and they broke trail.

"And how well I remember those first few years with father breaking prairie. Brother and I following up with our hatchets, chopping in corn every fourth furrow, stopping *occasionally to dig out an Indian biscuit to eat. They were very good.*

"Our first Sunday School was organized in our school house by a Mr. Frady a missionary. There were no doctors closer than Millerboro and when mother became so ill, grandma and grandpa Carver doctored her. We children, white faced and scared, huddled at the foot of the stairs, expecting to hear she was no more.

"Many and many nights mother and grandma Carver were called out, often in storm to help some other sick woman, and not always successful. The first funeral was that of a stranger by the name of Johnny More, who was staying at Ben Jones. They laid out a little cemetery on Mr. Carver's land and Mr. Carver was called on to make many pine boxes that were buried on that lonely hill. But neighbors were really neighbors then.

"We used to have dances, singing in schools and literaries. Father would load us all in the bob sled, take an axe along to cut the ice out of the fords, and what fun we had. Everyone had to make a crowd. We were lucky if we could get Mr. Chet Fields and Ed to play for our dances, or Nell Sparks. We often had some one who only played about three times. At other times father would load us all up and drive to some neighbors to spend the night. The older folks playing cards, singing songs and visiting. We children kept fire and maybe popcorn. For midnight lunch we would probably have mush and milk.

"In referring to the Indian scare, father was away that year. Spencer our only man of the house at the time was bout 14 years old. A mail man had ridden throughout with the report that Indians were on the war path and coming our way. Some of the families went to Creighton, but uncle and other neighbors said they would see no harm come to us. Mother's eyes were almost glued to the west hills, expecting to see them come swarming down on us.

"The only Christmas of my childhood, when Santa could

not brave the storms and come to our house, mother was equal to even that. We had popcorn balls and taffy candy. The little girls had rag dolls and we older ones red mittens that she had knit."

By Anna Haskin Buchanan
Orchard News 1937

The wagon was stuck. This was the sixth time today and it was only 10:30 in the morning. "Damn these rains," Edwin Haskin muttered to himself. Edwin, the eldest son of Samuel Jenny Haskin, was no stranger to hardship. He had been a mail carrier in Wisconsin for many years and he delivered mail through all kinds of harsh conditions. He had also voluntarily enlisted in the army at the age of 17. He served with Company F of the 11th Infantry of Wisconsin during the Civil War. During the two years and seven months that he served, he saw his share of hardship. Nevertheless, falling into a mud hole every 15 minutes was certainly testing his resolve, if not trying his patience.

Edwin and his family had been on the trail to Nebraska for about two weeks now. If it had not rained daily, it sure seemed like it had. Edwin, his wife Delia, and their five children left Wisconsin on April 10th with a covered wagon pulled by two old horses. The trip had not been an easy one, but neither his wife nor his children had complained. Spencer was his oldest child and even though he was only 12, he seemed much older. Next, there was Anna. At nine-years old, she was slender with dark hair. Then there was Clarence, who was a sandy-haired bundle of four-year old energy. Clarence did not care about the mud. More often than not, he had more mud on him than there was on the trail. Millie had just turned three-years old and she did not like the mud or the rain. Last, there was baby Cora. She was only a couple of months old and she seemingly did not care one way or the other.

As the rest of the family watched from the driest grassy patch that they could find near this latest obstacle that had claimed their wagon, Edwin, Spencer, and two tired, old horses labored to pull the wagon from the sticky muck. Within minutes, the wagon was free. Edwin loaded his wife, Cora, and Millie back into the wagon. He carefully inspected his horses. They could not take much more of this. They were tired, wet, and miserable. There was a town several miles ahead. Perhaps there he would be able to purchase another horse. He hoped that a third horse would be able to take the strain off the other two. Thus, without further delay, they were off once again. Delia and the two youngest children rode in the wagon while Edwin and the three older children walked.

Somehow, they made it to the next town without falling into another hole. They drove up to the local livery stable, purchased another horse, and once again were on their way west. That afternoon, they encountered several more mud pits, but the third horse made the experience a little less painful for all concerned. As the days went by, they made much better time. On May 21st, after nearly six weeks on the trail, they pulled up to the Samuel Haskin homestead on the banks of the Verdigris River.

Samuel and Annie were thrilled to see Edwin and his family again. Millie was only one-year old when they last saw her and this was the first time they saw baby Cora. Wallis, Maria Sophia, Mercedes, and Florence came for supper that evening. Samuel loved having his grandchildren around. After supper, the men sat outside of the dugout while the women cleared the kitchen table and washed dishes. As the men looked out over the Verdigris River, Samuel turned to Edwin, his pipe in his hand, and asked, "Well, my boy, what do you think?"

Edwin looked out over the wooded valley and then over at the hills to the north and to the west then replied, "I can see why you like it here."

Samuel took a couple puffs on his pipe and nodded. He knew that Edwin would love it here too.

The next day Delia's brothers Watts and Tite Sherman came for a visit. That morning, the Shermans and Samuel showed Edwin some land south and east of Wallis' place. Edwin liked what he saw so they staked out the corners and Edwin took off for the land office at Niobrara to file claim. While Edwin was gone, his family stayed with Julia Griffith. Once Edwin returned from the land office, he was off to Yankton for the goods he had shipped from Wisconsin. On his way, he would have some lumber shipped from sawmills along the Niobrara River. He could have had timber shipped from Yankton much cheaper than the lumber, but he insisted on having a wood frame house instead of a log cabin. While Edwin was gone for lumber and supplies, his family continued to stay with Julia.

On June 4th, 1878, Delphine Rabuck married Elroy Crum. Del had been seeing him frequently since he gave her a ride to her grandparents' place the day she arrived in Nebraska. The marriage took place at Sam and Annie's and afterwards, Shib Carver hosted a dance. All the neighbors enjoyed the evening of food, drink, music, and fun.

During the summer of 1878, Edwin, with the help of his father, brother, and brothers-in-law, built the first wood frame house in Sherman Precinct. By the end of the summer, Edwin's house was finished and his family settled in to their new home. There still were not many people coming in to the area despite the large amount of land that was still available. William Sherman, a farmer from Iowa, staked claim to a homestead south of Wallis Haskin and filed for a tree claim on the land north of Samuel Haskin. Edwin filed for a tree claim on some nearby land, as did Wallis. The men then took to planting cottonwoods and a few fruit trees on their timber claims.

In August, Samuel made a trip to Niobrara for some supplies. While in Niobrara, he ordered some lumber to be delivered into the Verdigris River valley. The settlers had convinced Samuel to build a general store and he knew that it would certainly be a convenience for everyone in the valley. The lumber would be delivered to him within the next week. If winter weather would just hold off until December, Samuel knew that he could have his general store nearly completed.

On his way back from Niobrara, Samuel encountered some troops form Fort Randall. They were on orders to find and remove any Indians that remained in the area. For some reason the State felt that the presence of Indians hindered the settlement. Samuel knew better. There had not been an Indian raid in the area for over two years. The railroad land controversy and lawsuit, however, was doing more to slow the settlement of the area than the Indians were. Samuel thought to himself that the troops should spend their time removing the railroad lawsuit, instead of the Indians. Oh well, they had their orders. So, without comment, Samuel resumed his journey home.

As he rode into the valley, he stopped at the camp of Mon-e-ga-he. He told the Arrow Chief what he had seen and heard. Arrow Chief agreed with Samuel that it might be wise to move the camp to a spot where it was not so obvious. Samuel hated to see the Ponca camp move. They were close friends to the settlers in this valley and he hoped to continue that friendship.

Mon-e-ga-he wasted no time moving his camp into the Verdigris River valley three miles to the south. Samuel helped his friends set up their teepees in the new location. Several days after the Ponca camp moved from the hill to the east of the Haskin homestead, the troops came into the valley. Samuel told them that he had not seen any Indians in the area and sent them out of the valley to the west, hoping that they believed him. If they found Mon-e-ga-he's people, they would be re-located to Indian lands in another state. Samuel also realized that if the troops kept pushing, the Indians would eventually fight back.

A couple weeks later, Samuel read the news reports of some Cheyenne Indians that had escaped from a reservation in Oklahoma. Chiefs Little Wolf and Dull Knife led the escaped band. Troops had caught up with the escapees in Oklahoma, but after a short battle, the Indians were able to continue their flight northward and on into Kansas. On September 30th, the Cheyenne raided a settlement in Decatur County, Kansas, killing

18 people. Reportedly, the Cheyenne were headed toward Nebraska. Some of the settlers on the prairie were concerned, but Samuel reassured them that there should be no danger.

Figuring he could handle the Cheyenne if they should come this far to the north, Samuel did not give them another thought. Other things, that were more important, now required his immediate attention. He wasted no time beginning the construction of his general store, which was placed just west of his dugout and near the county line. With all the neighbors helping him, he figured the store would be ready to open by the first part of December.

The next week, as Samuel was working on the store, a man and woman pulled up in a covered wagon. Samuel could see that the wagon was heavily loaded with all their household goods. The man jumped down from the wagon and approached Samuel. "My name's Alexander McCollum," the man said. "Folks just call me Alex. And this is my wife, Evaline."

"I'm Sam Haskin. You folks just passin' through?"

"Na, I'm looking for a place to settle. Any land nearby?"

Samuel thought for a few seconds. "There's some land to the west here about half a mile."

Alex looked toward the west and beyond the Verdigris River. "I hate to impose, but would you have the time to show us?" he asked of Samuel.

"No imposition at all," Samuel replied. "Folks in these here parts help one another. Where are you from?"

"Ohio directly," Alex replied. "We heard about free land in Nebraska and thought we would give it a try."

Samuel showed Alex and Evaline to the land that bordered the west side of Cyrus Carver's homestead. The east branch of the Verdigris River flowed through the Carver land and the south branch of the river flowed on the west side of this unclaimed land. Alex and Evaline liked what they saw, so Samuel helped them locate the corners and jot down the legal description for Alex to take to the land office in Niobrara. Samuel was very concerned that it was a little late in the season for the McCollums to try to finish their home before the winter weather struck. "We have a boarding house over here to the south," Samuel told the McCollums. "I'm sure that Julia can put you up for a while. As soon as I'm finished with my store, me and my wife will be movin' into the rooms in back of it. My dugout will be empty, so you are welcome to stay there until your home is finished."

"That is very kind. As soon as I'm back from Niobrara, I'll begin cutting trees for a cabin," Alex exclaimed.

"I wouldn't recommend that," Samuel responded. "We have an agreement with the Ponca that we will not cut the trees. If that is a problem, perhaps you'll be better off looking for land somewhere else."

Samuel explained to Alex that they had no troubles with the Indians because they had agreed to certain terms. Since the settlers in the valley had followed those terms, not only did the Indians give the settlers no trouble, they actually helped the settlers when needed.

"I heard there had been some problems with the Indians from time to time," Alex stated.

"Not here," replied Samuel.

"What do you do for lumber?" Alex asked.

"You can arrange for logs or lumber to be delivered here when you go to Niobrara," Samuel stated. "And like I said, the boarding house can put you and your wife up until my store is done. Then you can move in to my dugout."

Samuel took Alex and Evaline to Julia's boarding house. Once Evaline had her goods unloaded, her husband drove off to Niobrara to file claim to their land and to order lumber for their house. Seeing that the McCollums were in Julia Griffith's capable hands, Samuel returned to working on his store.

By the middle of November, the store was nearly completed. All he needed was about one more week of good weather then he and Annie could move in. It had been a long day. Shib, Dor, and Cyrus had helped him until nearly 8:00pm. Annie fixed Samuel a quick supper. Shortly after supper,

82

Samuel and Annie decided to retire for the evening. Just as he was about to lie down in bed, he heard someone knocking on the door. It was William Sherman.

"Annie's needed," William said. "Some stranger turned up at the Ben Jones place yesterday. He's awful sick."

Annie wasted no time gathering her supplies of herbs and remedies. William helped her into his wagon and they raced off to the south. Ben Jones lived about three miles south of the Haskins and the trip took them about fifteen minutes. William helped Annie down from the wagon and she rushed to the door of Ben's cabin. As she entered, she saw that Delia Haskin and Mary Carver were already at the stranger's bedside. Annie noticed that the poor fellow was just a boy, probably no more than nineteen years of age. Annie leaned over the bed, placed her ear to the stranger's chest, and listened for a heartbeat. Unable to hear his heartbeat, she placed her hand on his wrist. Still she could not find a pulse. The stranger had died. She looked over to Ben Jones and shook her head.

Ben lowered his head. "He came wandering in here yesterday," he told her. "He was burning up. He said he hadn't ate anything for days."

"Do you know his name?" asked Annie.

"He said his name was Johnny Moore," Ben replied.

When Cyrus Carver and Samuel Haskin arrived a short time later, the men discussed laying out a cemetery. This was the first time there had been a death in the valley since William Griffith died five years before. Cyrus told the men that he would give a small portion of his land for a cemetery. Ben Jones and William Sherman helped Cyrus and Samuel place the body of Johnny Moore in Samuel's wagon. Samuel then helped Annie and Mary Carver into the wagon seat, and he and Cyrus drove to the Carver place. They placed the stranger's body on a bench in the Carver barn.

"I'll come in the morning to help you with the burial," Samuel told Cyrus.

The next morning, Samuel helped Cyrus locate some

land for the cemetery. On a hill north of Cyrus's cabin and just a short distance from the Antelope and Knox county line, they staked out four corners. Then, towards the northeast corner, they dug a grave for the young stranger who had died the night before. Ben Jones, William Sherman, Wallis Haskin, Ed Haskin, Delia Haskin, Cyrus Carver, Mary Carver, Annie Haskin, and Samuel gave Johnny Moore a proper burial. Cyrus placed a wooden cross, which he had fashioned earlier in the morning, at the head of the grave. "Johnny Moore, died 13 Nov, 1878," was carved into the arm of the cross. Delia spoke a few kind words over the grave of this young man that none of them knew. They knew not from where he came but they knew he was now in the loving arms of God.

With that unpleasant business finished, Samuel once again turned his attention to the completion of his store. So far, the weather was pleasant with cold nights and mild days. However, Samuel knew that would not last. Although he had only seen two winters in Nebraska, that was enough for him to know that they would soon see very cold temperatures and a good deal of snow. By the end of November, Samuel and Annie moved into the store and helped the McCollums move into Samuel's dugout.

December was snowy and cold, but Samuel had seen much worse. At least there had been no blizzards to endure. Samuel took advantage of sunny days during the second week of December and went to Yankton for some supplies to stock his store. All the settlers for miles around took advantage of the convenience and purchased all their necessary items from Samuel. Now, they still needed a post office and a school.

The winter of '78 and '79 had its share of cold and snow. However, it was not as bad as the winter before. About twice a month, the Carvers would hold a dance. One month the dances would be at the Cyrus Carver place and the next month they would be over to Shib's. During the weeks between the big Carver dances, Ben Jones or William Sherman would host a card party. Every Saturday night there was a dance, a card party, and sometimes a literary, all of which provided the settlers with much entertainment and amusement during the long, cold winter months.

That winter, the settlers also took steps to get a school and a post office. Samuel met with the County Superintendent and decided upon a spot on the Samuel Haskin property, west of the store on the county line, as the site for the first schoolhouse. Meanwhile, Edwin Haskin arranged for postal services. Since Edwin had previously carried mail, the government provided him with an application for a post office and assigned him to carry mail between Yankton and Clearwater. Edwin's contract would begin the first part of April. Edwin took the post office application to his father and tried to talk his father in to applying for the contract. However, Samuel had never operated a post office before and he was not interested. Both Samuel and Edwin felt that the post office should be close to the store and the school and, since Alex McCollum was building a house less than ½ mile west of the store, Samuel suggested that Edwin ask him.

Alex, also, had never operated a post office before, but was willing to give it a try. Edwin gave the application to Alex and helped him complete it. If accepted, Alex would be appointed as postmaster and be paid $1.00 per month. The application asked for a name for the post office. Alex asked Edwin and Samuel for their input, but neither one of them had any suggestions. Since he was born near a town called Jessup in Pennsylvania, he wrote "Jessup" as the name requested for the post office. After Alex filled out the application, he gave it to Edwin. The next week Edwin made a trip to Niobrara to order some logs for the new school and he mailed the application for Alex.

In January, settlers in the area received word that Cheyenne Chicf Dull Knife had come into Nebraska and had eluded some troops from Fort Robinson. Many of the settlers from the prairies were leaving their homes to seek safety in Creighton, Niobrara, and Neligh. Hearing the report, Samuel went to the village of Mon-e-ga-he. He related the report to the

Arrow Chief of the Ponca. "If Dull Knife makes it this far to the east," Samuel said, "I will try to talk to him."

"No," Arrow Chief told Samuel. "Dull Knife very desperate. He will not listen to Ke-ton-ga. If Dull Knife come, Ke-ton-ga come to Mon-e-ga-he. Mon-e-ga-he will stand with Ke-ton-ga and fight."

Arrow Chief told Samuel that his braves would begin patrols to guard against intrusion by Dull Knife. He recommended that Samuel do the same. Samuel returned to his people and assured them that they should stay, but they needed to keep careful watch. Edwin Haskin was gone to Niobrara for logs for the new school and his wife Delia was home alone with their children. Their oldest child, Spencer, was only 14 and Delia told Samuel that she was frightened. Samuel told her that she would be fine and he assured her that he and Wallis would see that no harm would come to them. A couple weeks later Samuel received word that Dull Knife and his band had been killed by troops from Fort Robinson.

February was very dry. Not one flake of snow fell during the entire month. The weather was perfect for construction, so Alex McCollum spent the month working on his house. Edwin, Wallis, and Samuel Haskin spent the month building the log schoolhouse and by the first part of March, they were finished. Within a couple weeks, Alex had finished his house and he and Evaline moved from Samuel's dugout into their new home. March was turning out to be nearly as dry as February. A small amount of snow fell on the fourth day of March, but it melted the next day.

The day after Alex and Evaline had moved into their new home, a spring thunderstorm developed to the west. A bolt of lightening struck the dry grasses on the prairie west of the Verdigris valley. The dry prairie was soon ablaze. The men from the valley loaded wagons with buckets of creek water, blankets, and shovels, and set out to fight the raging fire. The southwest winds drove the fire rapidly to the west banks of the valley. Then, the wind abruptly changed to the south and drove the fire along the valley's west side. The fire raced northward, burning everything in its path from grasses, to trees, and even cabins.

The men battled the blaze with wet blankets and shovels all to no avail. The parched prairie grasses were perfect fuel for the wind-driven inferno. As the fire headed to the north, men from Grimton and Walnut Grove joined the fight. The winds pushed the fire to the east of Walnut Grove, and the flames claimed several homesteads as it continued its relentless rampage northward. Samuel and the men from the Verdigris valley were pleased that the wind had changed just in time to protect their own homes, but they knew that there were other homes to the north that were right in the path of the oncoming fire. Samuel and his men, therefore, raced northward to assist those homesteads.

All night, and most of the next day, the men fought the fire. There seemed to be no stopping the angry blaze. A couple men from Walnut Grove lost their lives while trying to protect their homes. Finally, by late afternoon, the rains came and the weary men shouted for joy. The rains tamed the inferno just enough that those who were struggling to overcome it now had the upper hand. By evening, the fire was out. The blaze had burned a path nearly four miles in width and running from two miles south of the Antelope and Knox County line northward to almost a mile south of the Niobrara River. The fire had burned up to the very western edge of the Verdigris River valley.

Tired, but relieved, Samuel and his men returned to their homes that night. As Samuel entered his house, Annie stood at the door with tears flowing down her face. Samuel knew immediately that something terrible had happened. With a lump in his throat he asked Annie, "What's wrong?"

"John Brown is dead," she replied.

Samuel could not believe his ears. He had known John and Charlotte for many years. John had come with him from Wisconsin in 1873 to file their claims in Nebraska. They had eight children and two were married. But, what of their younger children? How would Charlotte manage?

Samuel hitched his horses to his wagon and helped Annie into the seat. They drove south to Wallis' cabin where Samuel informed Wallis about John. He asked Wallis to watch the place for a couple days because he and Annie were going to Walnut Grove to help Charlotte. Wallis told him not to worry and Samuel turned the wagon north and headed for Walnut Grove.

A couple days later, they laid John Brown to rest in a small cemetery at Grimton. Many of the settlers from the area were there. John was well liked and admired by all his neighbors. He died trying to protect a neighbor's cabin from the flames. He had always devoted his life to helping others and Samuel knew that John would never be forgotten by anyone who knew him.

Samuel and Annie stayed with Charlotte a couple days. Charlotte told them that she was going to sell John's homestead and move in with her daughter and son-in-law who owned a farm about a mile to the north. Samuel and Annie told Charlotte that if she needed anything, all she had to do was ask and they would help her anyway they could.
Charlotte appreciated the offer and assured her friends that she was going to be fine.

By the end of March, Alex McCollum received his appointment as the first postmaster of Jessup, Nebraska. Samuel christened both the school and the store with the same name as the post office. On April 1st, Edwin began his duties as mail carrier and was assigned to carry the mail from Yankton to Clearwater. Once each week he stopped at the Jessup Post Office with a mail delivery.

The first term at the Jessup School began the first week of April. Mrs. Viola Burton was the teacher. Her students were Jennie Sherman, Belle Sherman, Eva Sherman, Irma Sherman, Sylvia Sherman, Spencer Haskin, Anna Haskin, Loren Carver, Oliver Carver, Donnaly Carver, and Orland Carver. The first term of school ran until June 1st, 1879. The schoolhouse served a dual purpose for this little settlement because church services were also held in the little log cabin. Delia Haskin and Mary Carver took turns delivering the Sunday sermon. Sunday school was held for the children prior to the Church services and the women prepared lunch for the patrons at the end of services every Sunday.

Jessup was now on the map and seemed to have everything that any frontier town could ever need. It had a store, a school, a post office, a church, a boarding house, and a cemetery. Most importantly, Jessup had people who genuinely cared about each other and helped each other in times of need.

Edwin Ruthvan Haskin
Photo taken about 1880.
Haskin Family Photo.

Chapter 7 Growth and Death

An increased number of settlers began to pour into northeast Nebraska during the spring of 1879. By this time, all the counties in Nebraska, except for Antelope County, settled the lawsuit against the railroad brought forth by a judge in Omaha several years earlier. Settlers in the surrounding counties were now assured that they would own the land to which they filed claim after a period of five years. Since the Jessup Store was on the county line, Samuel sold goods and supplies to many families seeking land in the surrounding counties. Some settlers, however, were willing to take the risk and file on the odd numbered sections of land in Antelope County, despite the dispute with the railroad. A German immigrant by the name of Julius Hering was one of those brave souls.

Julius stopped at the store for supplies during the middle of April. He told Samuel that he was going to build a mill three miles to the south on the Verdigris River. He showed Samuel the spot he had chosen on a map. Samuel knew the spot very well and felt it would be an excellent location for a flourmill. The site Julius had selected was near the Ben Jones and Tite Sherman homesteads. Samuel told Julius that the farmers in the region would be pleased to have such a mill so close where they could sell their grain.

Julius related to Samuel how he had sawed all the lumber he needed for his mill while he worked in Omaha. However, by the time he was ready to come north, the railroad had appropriated all of his lumber. He seriously considered suing the railroad, but felt that action would prove time consuming and, in the end, fruitless. Samuel agreed.

"Would it be possible to place an order for lumber here and could it be delivered to me?" Julius asked Samuel.

"Sure," Samuel replied. "We can have lumber delivered to you from Niobrara by the first of the week."

As Samuel promised, within a week, the lumber arrived from the north and Julius Hering began building his mill.

91

Samuel would see much of this young German over the next few weeks. The Jessup General Store, being the closest, was Hering's main source of supplies.

Rains were sporadic during the spring of 1879. It was shaping up to be a very tough year for the farmers. Despite the grim outlook, the people of Jessup remained positive. One could always count on a dance at the Carver place to lift one's spirits. The Carvers put on a huge party and dance the middle of June. Folks from miles around came to enjoy the fine food, liquor, and music. Elroy and Delphine Crum brought a new friend from west of Creighton. Katie Goodman had just moved to the land that bordered the north side of the Crum farm. She and her younger brother, George Goodman, settled on a pre-emption, which required them to live on the land for six months. After that time, they could pay $2 per acre and the land was theirs. Other than her little brother, Katie had no other family that was nearby and Delphine knew, all too well, what it was like to be that young and alone. Delphine, herself, struck out on her own when she was just fifteen years old and remembered how frightened she had been. Perhaps it was because she understood Katie's situation or perhaps because the two girls had so much in common, whatever the reason, Del and Katie became fast friends.

Del figured the Carver dance would be the perfect time for Katie to meet some of the neighbors and make new friends. She introduced Katie to her grandparents who were very pleased to meet the young girl. Samuel asked Katie about her plans.

"Del tells me that she worked cleaning houses for a time in Iowa," Katie answered. "I am willing to clean houses or even work the fields and gardens."

Samuel was impressed with the young girl's attitude and knew that she would easily find work. The young sandy-haired girl had spunk and courage. Samuel knew that Julia Griffith could occasionally use some help at the boarding house, what with all the people passing through these days, Julia had all the boarders she could handle. Samuel, therefore, took the opportunity to introduce Katie to Julia. As he figured, Julia jumped at the opportunity to hire Katie for the housekeeping a couple days a week.

The Carver dances provided only brief respite from the harsh conditions faced by the people of Jessup that summer. What little rain fell in June, even less fell in July. The hot sun beat down relentlessly on the parched prairie soil and the crops withered and died. Some of the settlers from the prairies on both sides of the Verdigris valley simply lost all hope and moved on. Most of the settlers in the valley, however, decided to ride out the drought. For Samuel, the decision to stay was easy. Many times before, he had seen dry summers and a meager fall harvest and many times before, he had survived. He figured this year would be no different. He knew that if the folks of Jessup stuck together and helped each other, as they always had before, they would rise above any hardship.

The dry weather seemed to have very little effect, however, on the influx of homesteaders coming into the region. Several times each week wagons would stop at the Jessup Store for supplies and directions. Most were planning on heading south to the Elkhorn River or on west to O'Neill. Some were looking for land along the Verdigris River and some were looking for land on the prairies above the valley. No matter their preference, Samuel sold them whatever supplies they needed and gave them whatever help they required. He saw all kinds of people passing through the valley and knew that some had no idea what to expect. Those who were searching for an easy life on the Nebraska plains were soon to be very disappointed. Some, however, knew all too well, that the road ahead would not be easy. During one of the hottest days in July, as Samuel worked at building a tack shed near his stable, a family of five pulled up in a covered wagon. "Got some water for some weary folk?" the stranger asked.

Samuel looked up at the stranger in the wagon. He appeared to be in his 30's or 40's, was of slender build, light brown hair, and long mustache. The lines on the stranger's face gave Samuel the impression that this man had seen his share of hard times and sorrow. Nodding, Samuel pointed the way to the well a little west of the stable.

"I thank you, kind sir." Without another word, the stranger drove his wagon to the well, watered his horses, and filled his water barrels. As his wife, his daughters, and his sister-in-law took their drinks and filled their canteens, he walked over to the shed where Samuel was working.

"Sir," he began, "I sure do thank you for your kindness."

"Think nothing of it," Samuel replied, removing the pipe from his mouth. "Where are you heading?"

"We're going to settle in these here parts somewhere," the stranger said. Then he pulled a folded map from his shirt pocket and showed Samuel where he wanted to stake claim.

Samuel looked at the map. "Yep, that's just right over here about six miles." He said, gesturing to the west.

"I thought we were close. What's this place called?"

"Jessup. My name's Samuel Haskin. I run the store here."

"Pleasure to meet you, Mr. Haskin. My name's Sylvanius L. Whitmore and over there at the wagon is my wife, Octavia, and daughters, Helen and Henrietta, and my wife's sister, Sarah."

As Sarah and Octavia and her daughters walked over to meet Samuel, Annie stepped out in front of the store. "Come on over and sit in the shade," Annie said, noticing that the strangers appeared exhausted.

Samuel placed his pipe back in his mouth then he and the Whitmores walked over to the shade of the store. Sylvanius told the Haskins that he had brought his family to Nebraska all the way from Vermont. It had been over thirty years since Samuel and Annie had left Vermont so they were full of questions and very anxious to hear about their old home state. The Haskins learned that the Whitmores were from a place in Vermont called Middletown. When Sam and Annie lived in Vermont, they lived very close to Middletown and were surprised that they had never met any of the Whitmore family or Octavia's family, the Parks.

The two families lost all track of time as they visited. Before they knew it, the sun hung low over the western hills. Octavia helped Annie fix supper and it was late by the time they finished their meal. Both Helen and Henrietta were nearly asleep in their chairs.

"Why don't you folks stay the night," said Annie. "We have a dugout over here east of the store. It's not much, but it is shelter and it's cool."

Sylvanius looked over to Octavia and Sarah. He knew that they could not go on tonight and Octavia agreed. She did not relish spending another night under their wagon, which had been the case most nights on their trip to Nebraska. Samuel showed them to the dugout then he helped Sylvanius stable the horses for the night.

The next morning, Samuel showed his new friends to their new home on the rolling hills six miles west of Jessup. Jumping down from the wagon, Sylvanius looked all around at the gentle rolling hills. From where he stood, he could see nearly ten miles in all directions.

"As beautiful as the Goddess, Venus!" he exclaimed.

Finally, by the end of July, the rains came to the parched prairies of northeast Nebraska. The few crops that had survived soaked up the much-needed moisture. Grasses and trees once again seemed to team with life. Leaves were full and green; birds sang their cheerful songs in the leafy boughs of the trees. Rabbits frolicked in the tall, flowing prairie grasses.

Settlers continued to pass through the valley on a daily basis. The Jessup Store was as busy as it had ever been. Samuel was a little surprised by one of the settlers who came to the store at the end of July. He was an older man which Samuel guessed to be in his mid 60's and his wife was nearing sixty. The couple had four children. Samuel figured the oldest boy was sixteen and thought the youngest girl was nearly ten. Most of the people coming through the valley were younger adults and it was rare to see older folk coming in search of free land. Cyrus and Mary Carver were older, but they had adult children who had settled here, as well as many old friends who had homesteaded nearby. Samuel and Annie also were no longer as young as they used to be. However, the Haskins and the Carvers had pioneered untamed lands several times in the past.

These folks had no adult children in the area, nor did they have any relatives or friends here. Some people came to Nebraska without understanding how difficult life would be as they tried to tame the reluctant prairie. However, Samuel had the impression that this man knew very well what hardships lay ahead as he began to start a home in this wild, and sometimes, unforgiving country.

"Name's Lucious," the old man told Samuel. "Lucious Kibbee. Meet my wife Hanna, and my boys, Joseph and Frank. Those there are my girls, Minerva and little Emily."

Lucious showed Samuel the map he had obtained from the land office in Niobrara, and pointed to a spot along the headwaters of the south branch of the Verdigris. "This is where we wish to stake claim."

The Kibbees followed Samuel to the head waters of the south branch of the Verdigris River, nearly five miles southwest of Jessup. Lucious and his son, Joseph, walked the land and saw there were two springs flowing out of the hills. The springs met a couple hundred yards from where they began and gave birth to a small stream. Farther to the northeast, another spring flowed from the hillside and into the stream, which then cut its way through the rolling hills toward the north and east. Lucious liked what he saw, so he and Joseph located the corners of the property.

"This will do just fine," Lucious told Samuel. "We'll be headin' to Nibrary directly to file."

Samuel was about to ride back toward Jessup, when Joseph stopped him. "Mr. Haskin, I was wondering, after we get built and settled in here, could you use some help over there at your farm?"

Samuel was getting older and he certainly could not do his work as fast as he once had. Plus, there was still a lot of building to do around the place in addition to all the farm work. Wallis was busy with his own farm and Edwin was gone on the mail route most of the time. Maybe it would not be such a bad idea to have a hired hand. Joseph was a handsome, dark haired, muscular youth and he seemed to be quite handy. Samuel noticed the boy's calloused hands and figured the youth was quite accustomed to hard work.

"Tell you what, boy," Samuel answered, "come on over in a couple days and we'll talk."

The dry summer and sparse harvest were not enough to discourage the settlers of the Verdigris valley. However, the prairies, hills, and valleys of northeast Nebraska were not about to yield easily to development. As if the hardships of the summer were not enough, an early winter storm set its sights on Jessup and the surrounding region. The blizzard hit early in November. The relentless wind piled the snow into drifts nearly ten feet tall. Then, if the snow and wind were not enough, the temperature plummeted below zero for days. Even still, the people of Jessup prevailed.

When the weather broke, Samuel hitched his horses to his buckboard and set off for Niobrara to replenish the supplies for his store. With the recent winter storm, all the wagons and drivers from the Niobrara trading post were busy delivering supplies to surrounding communities. Needing to return to Jessup immediately with two wagon loads of supplies, and having but one wagon, Samuel sought to hire another.

A Frenchman by the name of Louis Morsett had a wagon and was available. Louis brought his family to Niobrara earlier in the fall, but figured he had arrived in Nebraska a little too late in the year to find some land, stake claim, and build a proper shelter for his family before winter set in. He, therefore, decided to stay in Niobrara for the winter, work some odd jobs, and seek a homestead in the spring.

With the help of Louis and his wagon, Samuel returned

to Jessup with enough supplies to last for a couple months. Louis had never been so far to the south along the Verdigris River. He liked what he saw and asked Samuel about any available land. Samuel told him that most of the available land was railroad land, which was currently under dispute by Antelope County officials. The land was there, and claim could be filed, but there was no certainty whether the claim would be honored when the dispute between the county and the railroad was finally settled. Samuel let Louis know that it was entirely his decision, but it was a huge risk.

"I'll have to give it some thought," Louis said in a heavy French accent. "Who knows, mon ami, we may yet meet again."

On December 27th, Samuel and Annie Haskin became great, grandparents for the first time. Their granddaughter Della Crum gave birth to a little boy named Frank Emerald. Anxious to meet the newest addition to their family, Sam and Annie drove their wagon to the Crum farm west of Creighton to see their new great, grandson on the first day of the new year.

Then, on February 8th, 1880, Wallis and Maria Sophia welcomed a new baby boy that they named Elmer Francis. Annie stayed with Wallis and Maria Sophia for a week and helped care for Mercedes and Florence. Mercedes, now four years old, and Florence, who had just turned three, were both very proud of their baby brother.

The harsh winter finally gave in and spring came joyously to the hills and valleys that surrounded Jessup. Joseph Kibbee began working for Samuel a couple days a week. Jo, as Samuel called him, helped with the planting. When Jo was not helping Samuel, he was working on his father's farm.

That spring, two more post office contracts were granted to settlements near Jessup. Sylvanius L. Whitmore built a general store on his homestead and was granted a contract for a post office, which he named "Venus" for the beauty of the surrounding countryside. Several miles to the south of Venus, near the Kibbee homestead, a general store and post office was built and given the name "Glenalpine."

Meanwhile, Samuel was delighted, although somewhat surprised, to see Louis Morsett, his wife Philomone, and their seven children file claim to the land just west of Alex McCollum. Louis was not at all discouraged by the railroad land dispute and he was anxious to leave Niobrara. Town life did not suit him and he liked what he saw along the banks of the Verdigris.

Samuel was also pleased to see Julius Hering's mill nearly completed. Hering's wife, Ida, and children came up from Omaha with Ida's brother Hub Fields earlier in the spring. By fall, the mill would be ready for grain.

Before summer, some railroad surveyors came into the valley. There were plans to build a rail line from Canada to Mexico, and they were considering running the line somewhere through the Verdigris River valley. The railroad was on everyone's mind. If a line were to be built in the valley, it would bring rapid development and would open up a world of possibilities for the area. With a railroad, Jessup would no longer be isolated from the rest of the world.

Rains were plentiful during the summer of 1880. With adequate moisture, the crops brought in a bountiful harvest in the fall. Julius Hering's mill, called the Jessup Roller Mills, was in full operation, and served farmers from several miles in all directions.

On November 7th, Annie heard the rapid approach of horse hooves. She called to Samuel who was at his desk in the back of the store. As Samuel stepped out the door, Joseph Kibbee pulled his horse to an abrupt stop and jumped off.

"Father's dead," he blurted out as he tried to catch his breath.

Lucious Kibbee had collapsed that morning while feeding his horses. There was nothing that could be done. He must have died instantly.

Early the next morning, the Kibbee family along with neighbors and friends, laid Lucious to rest in the Carver Cemetery. The hills, prairies, and valleys of northeast Nebraska did not discriminate. Their unforgiving nature was no easier on the aged than it was on the young. For nearly 65 years, Lucious was no stranger to hardship. Having previously tamed the prairies of Kansas and Iowa, he felt no apprehension about once again settling virgin lands. It was a little over a year since Lucious and his family arrived and, in that time, he had made a nice home for his family.

With his father gone, Joseph, as the oldest son, now bore the responsibility of providing for his mother and siblings. Tirelessly, Joseph worked his father's claim while still working two days a week for Samuel. Not once did he complain, nor did he falter in his commitments. As the months went by, Samuel came to think upon Joseph as he would a son. In turn, it seemed that Joseph relied upon Samuel for encouragement and guidance, much as he would his own father.

During the spring of 1881, the Brandts and the Rabucks left Wisconsin. Frederick and Mary Rabuck moved their family to Redfield, Dakota, while Fred and Sophia Brandt took a homestead in Knox County, Nebraska about 1/2 mile east of the Jessup General Store. Maria Sophia was thrilled to see her family again. Her brothers and sisters were equally as thrilled to meet Mercedes, Florence, and baby Elmer. Maria Sophia's sister Sara was now married to John Gardner and they took claim to some land just north of Fred and Sophia Brandt.

That fall, Della Crum gave birth to her second son named Walter. It was a difficult birth. Samuel took Annie to the Crums to help with the delivery. Walter was never very healthy and, a few days after Thanksgiving, he died in the arms of his mother. They buried baby Walter in the little cemetery on the hill west of the Jessup Store. Elroy and Della took the death of their baby very hard.

Annie stayed with the Crums until she, herself, took ill the middle of December. Mary Carver and Delia Haskin took turns helping Samuel care for his ailing wife. Annie had been at Samuel's side through the good times and the bad. She was his rock and his strength and Samuel could not bear the thought of losing his Annie.

On Christmas day, the Haskin family all gathered at Samuel's place. Delia and Maria Sophia fixed the dinner. Elroy, Della, and Frank came from Creighton. Annie was feeling better and was able to get out of bed. Although she insisted on helping with the preparation of the meal, Delia and Maria Sophia protested. Annie felt that Maria Sophia should be resting because she was heavy with child. However, Annie was still very tired and very weak so she consented to let the girls take care of everything. Annie so enjoyed the grandchildren and Samuel hoped she would soon be well again.

On January 5th, 1882, Wallis and Maria Sophia welcomed baby Gerdula May into their family. Annie asked Samuel to take her to see the new baby. Samuel did not like the idea of taking Annie out into the cold, but he knew that there was no point in arguing, Annie's mind was set. Although Annie enjoyed seeing her new granddaughter, the trip and the cold air exhausted her. After an hour, she was ready to go home.

When they arrived back home, Samuel nearly had to carry his wife to the house. Once they were in the house, he helped her into bed. Annie would never again get out of her bed. She died peacefully in her sleep on February 1st with Samuel sitting at her bedside holding her hand.

Wallis Haskin Log Cabin
Photo taken 1876.
Haskin Family Photo.

Chapter 8   Women and Politics

A crowd of mourners gathered at the little Carver Cemetery on the hill to the west of the Jessup Store. Friends, neighbors, and relatives joined to pay their final respects to a woman they all admired. Mon-e-ga-he and his people came from their village to the south to honor the woman they called Mi-ta-in (the Crescent Moon).

Annie's husband and children stood solemnly beside her grave. Annie had been a good wife, a good mother, a good grandmother, and a good friend. Mon-e-ga-he's people sang to the spirits. Cyrus Carver stood beside his good friend, Samuel. Cyrus had carefully crafted the casket from pine and skillfully carved the inscription on the wooden grave marker. Edwin Haskin's wife, Delia, spoke a few words as Annie was lowered into her final resting place. Annie was buried next to the spot where they had buried her great grandson, Walter, only a few weeks before.

In a buckboard on a distant hill, a young man and his mother sat quietly watching the funeral. Elizabeth Dalrymple lost her first husband, Lyman Fields, during the Civil War. He was a private in the infantry in Virginia and died in battle on June 18, 1862. A desire to be near friends led her west to Wisconsin where she met and married Joseph Dalrymple. Upon Joseph's premature death, she moved to Nebraska in hopes of starting a new life in a new land. She earned a meager living by mending and making all sorts of clothes and her son, Charles Fields, earned money painting. Between the two of them, they earned enough money to survive. Annie had befriended Elizabeth when she moved to Wisconsin and had remained a close friend ever since.

As friends and neighbors slowly departed from the little cemetery on the hill, Charlie Fields turned his wagon and drove toward the Jessup Store. When they pulled up to the store, Charlie helped his mother from the wagon, took a couple bags from the back, and placed them on the ground. Charlie then climbed back into the wagon and drove off to the south. Elizabeth took her bags and walked up to the store, found a chair, sat down and waited.

When Samuel arrived with Wallis and Maria Sophia, he was somewhat surprised to find Elizabeth Dalrymple waiting at the front of the store. "I heard about Annie," she said. "I thought you may need some help with the store and things for a time."

Samuel seemed pleased, but Wallis did not like it. Although he said nothing to his father, he was going to keep an eye on things. While Wallis had known Joseph Dalrymple, he really did not know Elizabeth very well. When both families lived in Wisconsin, the Dalrymples would come to visit the Haskins two or three times a year. After Joseph died and Elizabeth moved to Nebraska, she kept in touch with Annie through frequent letters. However, after the Haskins came to Nebraska, she never once came into the valley to see them. Wallis felt that it was very strange that Elizabeth show up on the day of his mother's funeral and offer her assistance.

Elizabeth moved in with Samuel and helped him with the general store. She did his housekeeping, his laundry, and cooked his meals. She also continued her work as a seamstress. Twice a month, her son, Charlie, would bring her clothing to mend or orders from some of her customers in Neligh for new clothing. He would then pick up those orders on his next visit and deliver them back to Neligh.

Samuel tried to keep himself busy. The loss of his daughter, Raviah, several years earlier was almost more than he could stand. He thought he had finally come to be at peace with her death. However, with the death of his beloved wife, the wound that he thought had healed was now ripped open one more time. A large mountain of a man who at one time could handle most anything that came his way, now seemed very vulnerable. Thus, Samuel stayed busy from first light of the morning until the last vestige of light in the evening.

As Samuel struggled to overcome this latest blow, he

found himself drawing closer to Elizabeth. While she could never replace Annie, her presence seemed to fill a portion of the emptiness that he felt within. As the weeks rolled by, he came to rely on her much the way he had with Annie. Perhaps it was because he was in so much pain over the loss of his wife, or perhaps he just did not want to see, but whatever the reason, he seemed oblivious to the protests of his family and neighbors over his relationship with Elizabeth. Wallis and Edwin did not trust her and they repeatedly cautioned Samuel not to get too close to her. Nevertheless, he needed a woman and Elizabeth had given him love and understanding when he needed it the most. Then on June 28th, 1882, he took Elizabeth to Niobrara and they were married. Within weeks after the wedding, Samuel signed his homestead over to his new wife as part of a bargain that if anything should happen to him, the homestead would provide for her.

As the months passed, Samuel began to feel more like his old self. Katie Goodman brought her new baby over for everyone to see at the end of August. She had a little girl that she named Mary Ellen. Samuel could not get over just how Julia Griffith made over the baby as if it were her own grandchild. Somehow, the birth of this little girl seemed to spark some life back into Samuel.

As autumn descended upon the valley, everyone turned their attentions and energies to the harvest. Corn was picked and husked, potatoes dug, cane chopped, hay cut and stacked, and molasses made. Everyone, male or female, young or old, had to do his or her share during harvest time. Basic survival was the payoff for the backbreaking labors in this harsh land. Failure to work meant no food to put on the table. No food on the table meant starvation, and starvation meant death.

Elizabeth did not realize the responsibilities of being a farm wife in the Verdigris River valley. Although she lived on several different farms over the course of her life, by her experience, the man did all the fieldwork and the woman did the housework. Such was not the case on the banks of the Verdigris.

Here, the women had to work the fields just as the men. However, she did not wish to do any of the fieldwork. Samuel explained to her that if she lived on the homestead, she was needed to work the fields, just as the other women in the valley were doing.

Elizabeth tried her hand at picking corn, but did not pick fast enough to suit Samuel. Even still, he was very patient. However, her hands soon were cut and bleeding and she walked away from the field in disgust. She tried to dig potatoes, but tore her dress and ran to the house in tears. Chopping cane, she faired no better. She only managed to slice her leg. Samuel then put her to making molasses, but she cried herself to sleep at night from raw, blistered hands. Samuel felt sorry for her, but life in the valley was not easy and their very survival depended upon hard, backbreaking labor.

In November, Della's husband Elroy packed up his belongings and left. Samuel was devastated. Once again, he began to feel as if someone had ripped his very soul from his body. He wondered how Della would survive. He knew that the death of their baby, Walter, affected them deeply and neither Elroy nor Della were coping very well. It had put a great strain on their marriage. While Samuel knew they were having some problems, he never thought that Elroy would leave her. With a three-year old boy to support, she once again sought out housekeeping jobs. Samuel offered to give her some money, but she refused. She was intent upon making her own way and Samuel had to admire her for that.

That winter was very difficult for Samuel. It was a constant struggle for him. He worried about Della and he missed Annie. Despite Elizabeth's shortcomings in fieldwork, she excelled as a companion and stayed by his side through it all. If not for her, Samuel felt he would have just curled up and died. Through Elizabeth's support and with the coming of spring, Samuel began to feel a new sense of purpose.

As the days warmed, it was time to return to the fields to

plant the crops. Needing help with the planting, Samuel gave Elizabeth the choice of running the plow or planting the seed. Elizabeth became furious. She was not a beast of burden and did not want to be treated as such. Nevertheless, Samuel was persistent and Elizabeth saw that her husband was not about to back down from his stance on this issue. She, therefore, consented to plant the potatoes while Samuel ran the plow. She managed to plant for more than an hour before she slipped and fell into a furrow. That was it. Elizabeth had enough.

The next day, April 9th, Elizabeth took the buckboard and headed north. Arriving in Niobrara by afternoon, she took out a mortgage on the land that Samuel had homesteaded. Then, she went to the office of the Notary Public.

She returned Jessup the next day with the Notary, Elias Underwood, and some papers that she wanted Samuel to sign. She had drawn up an agreement where she would release all rights to the Haskin Homestead for a consideration of $150. The papers also released Samuel from any claims to lands owned by Elizabeth.

Samuel tried to prevail upon his wife that they could work out some other agreement about the farm work. However, she told Samuel that requiring a woman to plow fields and pick corn was inhuman and she could not bear to live like that. She told him that she was moving back to Neligh and if he decided to give up the farm, he could come live with her there. The farm was his life and seeing no other alternative, Samuel paid Elizabeth the $150 and signed the papers. In turn, she signed the Quit Claim deed to the homestead and handed it to Samuel. She then packed her clothes and belongings, climbed into Underwood's wagon, and left the valley forever.

It was very hard for Samuel to get his mind off Elizabeth. He kept thinking about what she had done to him. However, he did his best to set his mind to the business at hand. He still had his homestead and the store and there was always plenty of work to keep his mind occupied. In addition, he now had new neighbors. William Sherman had sold his tree claim just north of the Jessup Store to a German family by the name of Joerissen.

Charles Joerissen was a small man with dark hair and a long, dark beard. His wife Christiana was a petite, cultured woman and, when you saw her, you knew that she was exemplary. Although she was an invalid, one would hardly notice because of her outgoing personality and her seemingly high intelligence. The Joerissens had a foster daughter named Emma Koehler. Emma's parents died in 1879 and she had been living with the Joerissens ever since. Charles and his family had come to Nebraska from New York and lived in Nebraska City for a while. However, Charles longed to own a farm, so they headed north. As they entered the Verdigris River valley, they were awestruck by its beauty and knew that this was where they wanted to be.

Charles and Samuel became fast friends and Samuel knew that Christiana would bring a touch of culture to the valley that, up until now, had been lacking. Their daughter, Emma, was the same age as Wallis's oldest daughter, Mercedes, and it did not take very long for the two girls to become friends.

Samuel and Wallis helped the Joerissens build their log cabin to the north of Samuel's stable. When the cabin was finished, all the neighbors came for a house warming. The Carvers provided the music for the dance and, despite his recent experience with Elizabeth, Samuel felt like living again. After all, he had to admit that it was very hard to feel sorry for himself when he had such wonderful neighbors as these folks at Jessup.

The railroad surveyors came through once again that summer. They spent three weeks in the valley taking measurements and notes. It now seemed certain that a rail line would run somewhere near Jessup. For at least a month, the railroad was the main topic of conversation for all the settlers for miles around.

Come fall, everyone was busy with the harvest and storing away food for the coming winter. Della received a letter from her father, Frederick Rabuck, asking her to come live at Redfield. Frederick thought that she would have better work in

Dakota. Plus, Frederick and Mary would be able to care for Frank while Della worked.

Della showed the letter to her grandfather. She did not want to leave him, especially now. However, Samuel assured her that he would be fine and that her father was correct. As Della left northeast Nebraska, she was excited to be heading for a new life, yet she worried about leaving her grandfather behind.

Samuel was very sad to see her go. In many ways, she was so much like her mother. She was a very independent and a very strong woman. Nevertheless, Samuel was glad she had finally matured enough to reconcile with her father. She had grown up considerably in the few short years that she spent here in Nebraska.

Come spring, Samuel once again hired Joseph Kibbee to help him with the farm. Between the two of them, they planted all the crops, operated the store, built a milk barn, and expanded the livery stable. Joseph's younger brother, Frank, was now old enough to work the Kibbee farm, so Joseph had more time to work for Samuel.

In March, Joseph married William Sherman's daughter, Sylvia. Then, he purchased some land a mile north of the Samuel Haskin homestead and began building their new house. Since his father's death, he had been dividing his time working on his family's farm and working for Samuel. However, he felt his younger brother should take on most of the responsibility for the family farm and Joseph, at 23 years of age, was ready to make a life for himself.

At the end of June, Samuel received a letter from his granddaughter, Del Crum. In her letter, she said that she was doing very well and that she was now getting along with her father's wife. She was no longer working, however, because she was now married to a man ten years her senior. She had met Charles Lamphere several months earlier and they were married on June 15th. Charles was very good to both her and her son, Frank. She wrote that she missed her grandfather and hoped to come back to Nebraska to visit him sometime soon. Samuel was pleased to learn that Del was now married and very happy.

Samuel's happiness for his granddaughter was replaced by concern for his son when Edwin arrived during the first part of July to let him know that Delia had filed for divorce. Samuel could not believe it. Several months earlier, Edwin had purchased some land west of Creighton and was staying there most of the time because it was a central spot on his mail route. Samuel told his son that he would go with him to speak with Delia.

As Samuel suspected, Edwin's wife thought that he was being unfaithful to her and she did not like him being gone so much. Edwin explained to Delia that his land near Creighton was the best place for him to stay during the week while he ran this mail route. He invited her to stay with him in Creighton on the nights that he was there. She agreed and the next day she went to Neligh and had the divorce case dismissed.

On August 23rd, 1884, Wallis and Maria Sophia had another baby boy that they named Julius Eugene. Their daughters, Mercedes and Florence, were both school age now. However, Elmer would not start school until the next spring and Gerdula was only 2 years old. Maria Sophia kept herself busy taking care of the cabin and the children.

Wallis still had to make trips to Niobrara for his father nearly once a month and sometimes he had to go as far as Yankton. As always, he would ask his Ponca friends to keep an eye on his place and his "white squaw." Maria Sophia was still uncertain of the intentions of the Ponca, while Wallis was away, and they still frightened her as they walked up to the cabin. Now, before Wallis would leave, he would tell the Ponca, "watch out for my place, but please don't scare my wife." Therefore, the Ponca would walk by the place daily, but they would not look toward the cabin. Instead, they would look straight ahead for fear of frightening Maria Sophia.

Shon-ge-ska, who had frightened Maria Sophia several years earlier by picking up Mercedes from her cradle while she was crying, came to the Wallis Haskin cabin frequently. The children loved him. Even Maria Sophia was becoming used to his presence. She began baking him apple and plum pies, which he loved. Sometimes he would go hunting with Wallis and they would bring back deer meat for Maria Sophia to cook. Slowly, Maria Sophia began to accept the presence of the Ponca and gradually her fear of them disappeared.

A few days after Julius was born, Maria Sophia's sister, Mary, moved into the Wallis Haskin cabin to help her sister take care of the children and to help with the housework. Of all Maria Sophia's sisters, Mary was her favorite. When they lived in Wisconsin, she and Mary were always together. It would be great having Mary living with them, and the children so enjoyed having their Aunt Mary around. She played games with them and was a lot of fun, and Maria Sophia thought that life could not be better.

While Mary was settling in at the Wallis Haskin cabin, things at Julia Griffith's boarding house took a turn for the worse. Julia was becoming very forgetful. She would forget where she placed things, she would forget to fix meals, and she had neglected to pay her property taxes for the year.

Katie Goodman was still working for Julia a couple days a week and, at first, she had not noticed a problem. However, when Katie discovered an unopened letter from the County requesting payment of the taxes, she thought something was unusual. Year after year, Julia always paid her taxes on time. Katie talked to Julia about the taxes, but Julia did not seem concerned. Not knowing what else to do, Katie spoke with Samuel. Between the two of them, they convinced Julia that she needed to get her taxes paid.

Over the next couple of weeks, Samuel kept a close eye on Julia. It was becoming apparent that she could no longer operate the boarding house on her own. Her mind was deteriorating rapidly. Samuel feared that without the income from the boarding house, Julia could not make a living. Therefore, he began to help Julia with the housekeeping and with the bookwork.

In October, Edwin Haskin's oldest daughter, Anna, married Katie Goodman's brother, George. Anna was barely sixteen years old and George was only 20 years old. The newlyweds made their home at Creighton, George continued to farm, and Anna took care of Katie's little girl, Mary, while Katie worked.

Over the next few weeks, Julia's condition did not improve. The county was now threatening to put Julia in a sanitarium and take her homestead. Samuel thought if Julia had a competent adult living in the household and helping her with her affairs, that the county would back off. Therefore, Samuel moved in with her. Meanwhile, he wrote a letter to Julia's daughter, Media Brill, who lived in Rockford, Illinois.

"Noveber 20 1884
"Mrs. Media Brill
"Rokford Il
"Media
"Your mother is not doing well. You should come to Nebraska as soon as you can to help your mother take care of her afares. Rite now I am here helping her but you should come at once.
"Samuel J. Haskins
Jessup Ne"

By the end of January 1885, Samuel still had not heard from Julia's daughter and Julia's condition was not improving. There were days that she thought she was back in Wisconsin. During those times, she thought that Samuel was her second husband, William Griffith. Samuel drafted another letter to Media urging her to come to Nebraska.

As Samuel waited for Media's reply, things were beginning to unravel at the Wallis Haskin cabin. Mary had now been living with Wallis and Maria Sophia for nearly five months. At first, it seemed that this arrangement was strengthening the bond between Maria Sophia and Mary. However, the cabin was small, Mary was a very beautiful young woman, and Wallis was far from blind.

Wallis did not intend for anything to happen, at least not at first. Nevertheless, as the weeks went by, the temptation became too great to ignore. About three weeks after she moved in with Wallis and Maria Sophia, Mary followed Wallis to the barn. How could things get so out of hand? At first, Wallis was ashamed of what happened, and he tried to convince himself that he had done nothing wrong, as long as his wife did not find out.

By January, Maria Sophia started to notice that Mary seemed to be taking her afternoon strolls only when Wallis was working in the barn. One day she watched as her sister went out for a walk. Mary walked a short way to the south of the cabin then took a sharp turn and walked into the barn. Maria Sophia had just put Julius down in his crib and he was asleep. The other children were at home, so she asked eight-year old Mercedes to watch the younger children for a few minutes, then put on her jacket, and headed toward the barn.

When Maria Sophia entered the barn, she was shocked and angered by what she saw in front of her. In the hay, in passionate embrace and only partially clothed, she saw her husband and her sister. As she screamed, she grabbed the first object she could lay her hands on – a shovel. She swung the shovel, hitting Wallis square in the head. Both Mary and Wallis jumped up from the hay, as Maria Sophia took another blind swing with the shovel. Wallis tried to grab the shovel from his wife, but before he could, he took another good hit aside his head.

Maria Sophia Haskin was not very big, but she packed a big punch. Wallis reeled and fell back into the hay. Maria Sophia then turned her attentions to her sister and took a swing, but missed as Mary ducked. Before Maria Sophia could take another swing, Wallis grabbed her from behind and took the shovel from her.

"Get out of here!" Maria Sophia screamed to her sister.

Mary had just pulled her dress back into place and started

to say something, but before she could, Maria Sophia shouted, "I hate you! Get out of here! Get out of my house and stay out!"

Without a word, Mary left the barn. Wallis released his wife, but she ran out of the barn after her sister. Maria Sophia caught up with Mary as she was about to enter the cabin and jumped between her sister and the door. "Don't you ever step foot in this house again," Maria Sophia told her.

"But my clothes and things," Mary began.

"Get out of here," Maria Sophia demanded.

Crying, Mary headed north to her parents' house. As Mary left, Wallis approached his cabin, still trying to button his trousers. Maria Sophia saw him and she quickly entered the cabin and locked the door. Wallis spent the next two nights sleeping at his father's place. By the third night, Maria Sophia let him back into the cabin, but he had to sleep on the floor for the next week.

When Sophia Brandt came after Mary's things, she questioned Maria Sophia about what happened. All Mary had told her was that she had a fight with her sister. Maria Sophia did not want to talk about it either, so Sophia did not push the issue. She picked up Mary's things and left it alone. She figured the girls would eventually work it out. However, within a couple weeks, Mary could no longer hide the fact that she was several months pregnant. She had known for nearly two months that she was going to have a baby, and somehow had tried to convince herself that she could keep hiding her condition.

Now that she could no longer hide her pregnancy, she had to tell her parents what happened. Sophia was shocked, but now, at least, she understood why her two daughters were no longer on speaking terms. She wanted to be supportive of Mary. Still, she knew how Maria Sophia must feel, and knew that Maria Sophia would feel even worse when she learned that Mary was going to have Wallis' baby. Despite Sophia's desire to be supportive of Mary, Fred Brandt was not at all understanding or supportive. He was very angry and he kicked Mary out of his house. Sophia could not change her husband's mind, so she left too. Mary and her mother moved into the dugout where the Brandt family had lived before their house was completed.

When Maria Sophia learned from her mother that Mary was pregnant, she was furious. As her mother left, Maria Sophia grabbed a broom and ran to the barn where Wallis was working. When she entered the barn, she saw her husband working at his bench with his back toward her. Before he could turn around, she raised the broom over her head and swung with all her might. Wallis fell to the ground like a rock. As he rolled over and tried to rise, she hit him once again with the broom. Several more times, she swung the broom and a couple of times she actually connected with brutal force. Somehow, through the attack, Wallis was able to subdue her.

"What the hell is wrong with you?" shouted Wallis.

Maria Sophia was so furious, she was shaking, and she could hardly speak. "Mary, she's, she's pregnant." Maria Sophia fell to the ground sobbing.

Wallis could not believe what he had just heard. He tried to comfort his wife, but she wanted nothing to do with him. For several days, she would not speak to him. Oh, how he wished he could take back what he had done. He never meant to hurt his wife.

As Wallis struggled to keep his family together and Samuel struggled to keep the county from taking Julia's property, the very fabric of the settlement was about to be torn apart. There was now talk that the railroad was going to bypass Jessup, but would be built past the Jessup Roller Mills three miles to the south. George Brooks, a businessman from Bazile Mills, a town two miles north of Creighton, took notice. During the spring of 1885, Brooks made a sizable investment and built a large store adjacent to Hering's Mill.

He then hired Pete O'Malley, who had land south of the mill, to run the store. Samuel knew that this would take a little business away from him, but he felt that a little competition was a good thing. However, Samuel and the rest of the settlement was blindsided by George's next move. Brooks pulled strings with some friends he had in Washington, D.C. and had the Jessup Post Office contract taken from Alexander McCollum. Then, Brooks, himself, took over the contract and changed the location of the postal services to his store at the mill. Next, he appointed Pete O'Malley as postmaster of Jessup.

Alexander McCollum appealed to the government to reinstate his contract for postal services and the government refused. The little settlement on the county line had lost its post office and had lost its name. Samuel tried to keep a positive outlook, but everything that he and the others had worked so hard to build was now falling apart. Despite Samuel's urging to keep fighting, Alexander sold his land to a man named Edwin Buxton. Alexander and his wife, Evaline, then packed their belongings in their covered wagon and left the Verdigris River valley behind them, forever.

As the McCollums left the valley, a new life entered. Mary Brandt gave birth to a little girl that she named Maud. Fred Brandt still would not allow Mary to move back into the house, so Sophia, Mary, and Maud continued to live in the little dugout. Sophia hoped her husband would change his mind in time.

Samuel went to Neligh on April 11th, 1885 to file for divorce from Elizabeth. She had now been gone for more than two years and Samuel had heard nothing from her in all that time. He could now legally file for divorce on the grounds of desertion. The attorney firm of Holmes and White were highly recommended, so Samuel hired them to represent him in this matter.

A little over a month later, Samuel received word from his attorneys that Elizabeth filed her reply with the District Court through her attorney B. F. Admire. In her reply, Elizabeth admitted that she was married to Samuel, but claimed that he was neither a faithful nor a chaste husband. She denied each and every allegation in Samuel's petition and alleged that he was guilty of extreme and beastly cruelty toward her. She stated that she left him because she could not bear any more cruelty.

Elizabeth also stated that Samuel's homestead was worth $3,000 and that he was the owner of a tree claim, of which she did not know the value. Claiming that she was without means of support, she asked that, in addition to the divorce, the Court grant her alimony.

In Samuel's response to Elizabeth's reply, filed with the Court on May 26th, 1885, he denied any cruelty whatsoever toward Elizabeth. He also denied that his homestead was worth $3,000 and denied any ownership of a tree claim. Attached to his response, he entered, as evidence, the agreement that Elizabeth, herself, drew up more than two years earlier. That agreement provided proof that he gave Elizabeth $150, which he claimed was a fair and reasonable payment, and was in accordance with aggregate property values. He asked that the Court grant his divorce and release Elizabeth from any further claims to his property.

The District Court of Antelope County, based on the settlement agreement, which Elizabeth drew up of her own free will, found in favor of Samuel. The divorce was finalized, and Elizabeth could no longer claim any right to Samuel's property or possessions.

Sophia Rabuck Brandt
Haskin Family Photo.

Chapter 9   Mars

Media Brill was not going to come to Nebraska any time soon. Disappointed, Samuel folded the letter from Rockford, Illinois and put it in the pocket of his jacket. Now he had to figure out a way to save Julia's land. When Samuel last spoke with the Sheriff, he was giving Samuel two months to show that Julia had a family member in the household to see to her affairs. Six weeks had passed. Samuel was running out of time. There had to be some way to help her.

Samuel pulled his buckboard up to the front of Julia's boarding house. Julia was on the front step washing the windows. Lately, her condition was sporadic; she had her good days and bad days. Today was one of her good days. She looked up as Samuel stepped down from the buckboard. "Any letters from Media today?" she asked, just as she did every morning.

Samuel nodded.

"She's not coming is she?"

"No, she's not." Samuel took off his hat and lowered his massive frame into the bench that sat at the front of the boarding house. He had to think this thing through. There had to be an answer. If he could not come up with a solution, the county was going to place Julia in a sanitarium and put her land up for auction. In a couple weeks, harvest would be in full swing, which would bring men from the surrounding villages and the boarding house would be filled for about a month. Julia needed that income. It was the only way that she was going to be able to pay her winter bills – that is, if Samuel could find a way to keep the county satisfied.

He sure wished that William were still alive. No one would try to take the land if he were still here.

"That's it!" Samuel jumped up from the bench.

"What's it?" The sudden outburst had startled her.

"Well," Samuel began, "the Sheriff tells me you need a family member here to see to your affairs. And if you had a husband, then you would have a family member here."

At first, Julia was puzzled. Then it dawned on her just what he was saying. "Are you asking me to marry you?"

"Do you see any other way?"

That day, Samuel and Julia made the trip to Niobrara and, the very next day, Samuel rode to Neligh. Although the Sheriff was not at all amused by Samuel's solution to Julia's problem, there was nothing more he could do. The marriage was legal and Julia's homestead was saved.

After the harvest was over for the season, business dropped off at the boarding house. Now, only a young woman named Miss Fannie Burton rented a room during the weekdays. She was the new teacher at the little log schoolhouse which set on the county line. Julia's bad days now outnumbered her good ones. There were times when she did not even recognize Samuel. It was very difficult for him to handle all of Julia's affairs and his own as well. Katie Goodman was still coming to help two days a week and Joseph Kibbee helped as much as he could, while still helping his brother with the family farm and working his own farm.

Now that things were slow at the boarding house, Samuel turned his attention to getting the post office back. Edwin Haskin, having worked for the government as a mail carrier for years, helped his father contact the right people. However, there seemed to be nothing that they could do. They told Samuel that with the Jessup Post Office less than 3 miles away, they would not grant another contract for that part of Antelope County. All seemed lost.

During the first week of November, Samuel's good friend, Sylvanius Whitmore came for a visit. He had convinced his sister-in-law, Cynthia Jane Hubbard, and her three children to move from Vermont to Nebraska and he wondered if Samuel knew of any lands that were still available in the area. Samuel took him to some land to the west of William Sherman's place. Between the fact that it was very hilly and that it had been railroad land, no one had filed claim. Antelope County had just settled the lawsuit with the railroad and many of the odd numbered sections of land were now being snatched up at a rapid pace. For the most part, land seekers were looking for flat lands on the prairies, so the hilly lands were the last to be claimed.

Sylvanius feared that by the time his sister-in-law arrived in the spring, the land would be gone. "She's my wife's sister," he told Samuel. "Her name is Cynthia Hubbard. Her husband died in 1878 and left her with 3 young children."

"What happened to her husband?" enquired Samuel.

"Edmond Wilmont Hubbard enlisted in the Union Army in 1861," Sylvanius explained. "He served in Company G of the 22nd infantry from New York. He saw a lot of activity during the war. He fought at Antietam, Fredericksburg, and the second battle of Bull Run. He was discharged after being wounded in battle and, although the wound was serious, he just would not give in. He married Cynthia, had three children, and kept as active as possible. But, his wound finally killed him."

"It sounds like your sister-in-law has not had it very easy." Samuel reached into his jacket pocket for his pipe, but it was not there. He shook his head in disgust. Then he looked up at his friend who seemed a little worried.

Sylvanius noticed Samuel looking at him. "If the land is being taken as fast as you say, maybe it will be claimed by someone else before spring."

Samuel understood. "I know the land agent in Niobrara. You stake the corners, and take him the numbers. He'll give you the papers to send to your sister-in-law."

Sylvanius was relieved. Samuel helped his friend locate the corners and they headed back to Samuel's store. On the way back, Samuel told Sylvanius about his problem with the post office contract. Sylvanius knew all about the difficulties and politics involved when negotiating with the government.

"You say they told you that they would not grant another contract for Antelope County," Sylvanius advised. "But what about Knox County?"

"What do you mean?"

"Sam, why don't you see if you can get the post office north of your store? If you put a post office there, then it ain't in Antelope County. And, the closest post office in Knox County is mine, at Venus. And that ain't too close."

Perhaps Sylvanius had the right idea. Upon returning to his store, Samuel first located his pipe, filled the bowl with tobacco, struck a match, and then took a couple puffs. He then set down at his desk and composed a letter to the government. In his letter, he asked the government if they would consider granting a post office contract to that part of Knox County.

In December, Julia's health deteriorated. Samuel took her to a doctor in Neligh and, upon examination, the doctor recommended that Julia stay under his care for at least a week. After several days, Julia's condition improved and, a few days later, Samuel was able to take her back home.

Towards the middle of February, Samuel received a reply to his inquiry regarding the post office. His mighty hands were shaking as he hastily ripped opened the envelope. He took a couple deep breaths before he unfolded the papers to read the reply. Then, looking down at the sheets, he could hardly believe his eyes. The response was favorable! The government would consider granting a postal contract to someone in that area of Knox County. An application form had been included with the letter.

Now, Samuel had to find someone who would be willing to apply for the post office. The nearest people to the store were Charles Joerissen and a family that moved into the valley in November by the name of Morrill. Samuel did not know Moses Morrill very well, but he had known Charles Joerissen for nearly three years. Samuel looked out the north window of his store and saw Charles at the stable tending to the horses. Samuel grabbed his coat and hat and walked over to the stable.

Charles agreed to put in the application if Samuel would help him fill out the form. When Charles came to the question, "Name of Post Office," he looked up to Samuel. Both men knew that they could not name it "Jessup," because the mill stole that name from them.

"Well," Samuel took a couple puffs on his pipe. "If it wasn't for Sylvanius Whitmore, I might have just gave up the fight. He has the Venus Post Office. So, why don't we call this one 'Mars.' It seems fittin' to me."

On February 26th, 1886, Charles Joerissen sent in his application for the Mars Post Office. Now they would wait. The government could still deny the application, but it would probably be over a month before they would know. In the meantime, Samuel painted a new sign and placed it above the door of this store. The sign read, "The Mars General Store."

In March, the County Superintendent ordered the schoolhouse site moved to a central location within the district. Samuel failed in his attempt to delay the action until they received reply from their post office application. He felt that if there were a post office there on the county line, then the school could remain where it was. The County Superintendent agreed that if the settlement had its own post office, then the school could remain, but he refused to wait. Having no further legal recourse, Samuel, Wallis, and Joseph Kibbee moved the little log school house from the county line to the William Sherman place.

By the middle of April, Charles still had not heard back from his application. Samuel was beginning to think that the contract would be denied. He walked back to the boarding house and, as he was looking for the post office information he had received from the government, he noticed a paper in one of Julia's desk drawers. It was a will.

"In the name of God, amen. I, Julia A. Haskins, of the city of Neligh, in the County of Antelope, in the state of Nebraska, considering the uncertainty of this mortal life, and being of sound mind and memory, blessed be God for the same, do make and publish this my last will and testament, in manner and form following, that is to say:

"First. I give and bequeath to my beloved son Cyrus F.

Williams the sum of $5.00.

"Second. I give and bequeath all my personal property to my beloved husband, Samuel Haskins.

"Third. I give and Bequeath all my right, title and interest in my Homestead Entry No. 9415 situated near Jessup in the county of Antelope, in the state of Nebraska, to my beloved husband, Samuel Haskins.

"In witness whereof, I have hereunto subscribed my name this 26th day of December in the year of our Lord one thousand eight hundred and eighty five.

/s/ Julia Haskins

"We whose names are hereto subscribed, do hereby certify that Julia A. Haskins, the testator, subscribed her name to this instrument in our presence, and in the presence of each of us, and declared at the same time in our presence and hearing that this instrument was her last will and testament, and we at her request sign our names hereto in her presence as attesting witnesses.

/s/ Myra G. Krise,
City of Neligh, state
of Nebraska
Minnie J. Gilbert,
Loup City, Sherman
Co. Neb."

"Julia must have made this when she was at the doctor's back in December," Samuel said to himself. Then he asked Julia about it. She did not remember making out a will.

Julia was going to have to make out another will. First, he did not want her property, which he figured should go to her daughter, Media. Secondly, her son Cyrus Williams died as an infant, which would make probate on that part of the will impossible.

When Katie Goodman arrived for work that day, Samuel had her drive to Joerissens to pick up Christianna. When the two arrived, Samuel told Mrs. Joerissen about the will and asked her if she would help Julia make out another one. Mrs. Joerissen agreed, so Katie took Mrs. Joerissen and Julia to the Justice of the Peace who lived just a few miles to the north, to draw up another will.

"WILL OF REAL AND PERSONAL ESTATE.

"In the name of God, Amen. I, Julia A. Haskins of Vertigris Precinct in the County of Antelope, State of Nebraska of the age of 59 years being of sound mind, do make, publish and declare, this my last will and testament, in manner following, that is to say:

"First. I give and bequeath to my daughter, Meda A. Brill one Sewing Machine, one feather Bed, four Pillows, Brass kittle, one Rocking chair, two nice quilts, six sheets, one Looking glass, a quantity of glass Ware, one Revolver, one Cow and one yearling heifer, and one calf, one thousand feet of sideing, and lastly I bequeathe the rest of my Personal estate to my said daughter Meda A. Brill, whome I hereby appoint sole executrix of this my last will.

"In witness whereof, I have hereunto set my hand, this 14th day of April, in the year of our Lord, one thousand eight hundred and eighty six.

Julia A. Haskins

"The above instrument, consist of one sheet, was at the date thereof, signed and declared, by the said Julia A. Haskins as and for her last will and testament, in presence of us, who at her request and her presence, have subscribed our names as witnesses thereto.

/s/ C. Augusta Joerissen
/s/ Katie Goodman

"And lastly, I do hereby appoint my friend J.J.Sutton of Columbus Wisconsin, to be the executor of this my last will and testament, hereby revoking all former by me made.

/s/ Julia A. Haskins
/s/ Henry Rebmen, Justice
of Peace.

/s/ C. Augusta Joerissen, Jessup, Neb.
/s/ Katie Goodman, Creighton, Neb."

After the document was signed, Henry Rebmen sent it to Neligh to be filed with the County Clerk.

The next day, Charles Joerissen came running to the store. Samuel could see he was very excited over something. As he ran through the door he shouted, "We got it! We got it!"

At first, Samuel did not quite understand just what he was saying. Then, seeing the letter that he was waving in his hand, Samuel knew. They received their post office. It was official. Samuel's store was now officially The Mars General Store and their address would be Mars, Nebraska. That day, Charles began construction of a building to house the post office, but until the structure was completed, he would operate from his log cabin.

The following day, Sylvanius Whitmore drove up in his wagon and Samuel told him about the post office contract. Both joked about Nebraska now having Venus and Mars only six miles apart. Sylvanius invited Samuel to meet his sister-in-law and her children who had just moved to their homestead, which was west of William Sherman's place. Samuel climbed into the Whitmore wagon and the two friends rolled down the trail to the south.

As Whitmore and Haskin pulled up to the property, where Whitmore's sister-in-law filed claim, Samuel noticed that the new settlers appeared to have just arrived the day before. A covered wagon still sheltered all the family's belongings and a cooking fire burned near the wagon, which also served as shelter for this widowed mother and her three children.

Cynthia Jane Hubbard looked up from her cooking as the wagon pulled in. Seeing that it was her sister's husband, she called to her children. From the other side of the wagon, three teen-age children appeared. Nearly in unison, all three shouted, "Uncle Sylvanius!"

The oldest child, a small, slim girl of seventeen ran up to her uncle and gave him a hug. The two younger children, who were both boys, the oldest barely fifteen, smiled excitedly as they shook their uncle's hand.

Sylvanius turned to Samuel, "this is my good friend Sam Haskins." Then in turn, he introduced his sister-in-law, Cynthia Jane Hubbard and her three children: Annis, Eddie, and Arthur. When Sylvanius called the older boy "Eddie," Samuel saw a disapproving look on the boy's face.

"I'm Ed," the boy corrected.

Eddie took on a lot of responsibility several years earlier, when his father died. Through many hardships, he had to grow up long before his time. While in Vermont, he finished his schooling and then hired out to area farmers in order to help support his family. Samuel could tell that Ed was mature far beyond his young years.

Whitmore and Haskin spent the morning visiting with the Hubbards. Then, shortly before noon, the Whitmore wagon wound its way along the trail through the wooded valleys and back to the store at Mars.

A couple weeks later, Julia received a copy of her will. As Samuel examined the document, he noticed that it did not mention her homestead or the land that she owned in Minnesota. He knew that unless she specifically stated who was to receive those properties, the counties would dispose of them as they saw fit. She was going to have to amend her will, but she was no longer in any condition to travel.

The next morning, as Samuel was feeding Julia her breakfast, he heard a knock at the door. As he opened the door, he saw a young woman in her mid thirties, of slender build with dark brown hair.

"Are you the man that runs the store?" she asked.

"Yep," Samuel replied.

"Me and my husband are moving in just over the hill," she pointed to the south east. "We was in need of some supplies."

Just then, Katie Goodman pulled up in her wagon.

"Are you in a hurry?" Samuel asked the stranger.

"No," she replied.

"We have a matter that needs immediate attention," Samuel said. "Actually, we could use you as the second witness."

The stranger looked a little confused.

"By the way, my name's Sam. Sam Haskin. What do they call you?"

"Amelia Fay," the stranger replied.

When Katie walked up to the door, Samuel introduced her to Amelia then explained to her about the problem with the will. Katie, Amelia, and Samuel walked into the boarding house. As Samuel, with Amelia's help, wrote out an addition to Julia's will, Katie went to Julia's room. Julia was very weak, but she knew Katie, unlike most days over the past few weeks when she recognized neither Katie nor Samuel. When Samuel and Amelia entered the room, he explained to Julia that he wrote up an addition to her will, which would give her land in Minnesota and her homestead, here in Nebraska, to Media. He then explained to her that her previous will did not specify what she wanted done with the land.

Julia acted as if she understood so Samuel read her what he wrote and asked if she wanted anything changed. Weakly, she shook her head. Katie then handed Julia a quill and, with an unsteady hand, she placed her mark on the bottom of the paper. Katie and Amelia also signed as witnesses.

"Whereas, I, Julia A. Haskin of Verdigris Precinct, of Antelope Co. state of Nebraska, have made my last will and testament in writing, bearing the date of 14th day of April in the year of our Lord eighteen hundred and eighty-six. Now I do by this writing wish and decree that all my interest in the homestead upon which I reside shall be given to my daughter Media A. Brill. I also bequeath to the same my lots at Lake City, County of _____ state of Minn. As follows, 7 & 8 Block 95, and

lastly it is my desire that this my present Codicil be annexed to, and made a part of my last will and testament to all intents and purposes.

"In witness whereof, I have hereunto set my hand and seal this the 3d day of May in the year of our Lord eighteen hundred and eighty-six.

/s/ Julia Haskin

/s/ Amelia Fay, Mars, Neb
/s/ Katie Goodman, Creighton, Neb."

S. L. Whitmore
Haskin Family Photo.

Chapter 10   Where is Media?

"Julia my wife dide on the 6 and was bured on the 7th of May.   I went to Nealy on the 8th.   Caty Goodman comments worked kepen house May the 7th."

Author - Samuel J. Haskin

From the Journal of Samuel J. Haskin

As the morning breezes howled through the hills of Mars, Samuel knelt at Julia's bedside.   She had slipped into unconsciousness the morning before, at which time Samuel sent for the doctor from Creighton.   However, the doctor could do nothing for her.   He told Samuel to keep her comfortable. Samuel had been there all night sitting in a chair beside her bed and gently holding her frail hand.   Shortly after 7:00 am, she drew her last breath.   Samuel rose to his feet and gingerly placed a blanket over his wife.

Leaving the boarding house, Samuel walked to his stable, saddled a horse, and rode to the Carver place to tell Cyrus that Julia was dead.   Cyrus told him that a coffin would be ready by the afternoon.   Then, Samuel rode to the Wallis Haskin cabin to inform them of the sad news.   Delia Haskin was there to help Maria Sophia, who was soon to have another baby.

The next day, as Maria Sophia gave birth to a little boy named Walter Clarence, Julia was buried next to Annie Haskin in the little cemetery on the hill.   All the neighbors gathered to say their final goodbyes.   Julia struggled for years to make a life for herself in this valley and she had earned the admiration and respect of everyone who knew her.

After the funeral, Katie Goodman told Samuel that she had quit her jobs in Creighton so she could help him out full-time.   Samuel did not know how long he would keep the boarding house open.   Everything depended upon the length of time it would take to settle Julia's estate.   Nevertheless, he was pleased that Katie could now help daily.   The next day, Katie and her three-year old daughter, Mary Ellen, moved into the boarding house.

On May 8th, Samuel went to Neligh to request probate of Julia's estate. A telegram was sent to Julia's daughter, Media Brill, requesting her presence as executrix. Another telegram was sent to J. J. Sutton to request his presence to execute the will. The Court then scheduled the probate for May 16th.

Over the next few days, Samuel and Joseph Kibbee worked to build fences and pens for Samuel's livestock, which he had kept at Julia's place. When May 16th arrived, Samuel and Katie went to Neligh for probate of Julia's estate. In court, they learned that Media refused to serve as executrix and J. J. Sutton telegraphed to say that he could not be present for probate of the will. The Judge then rescheduled the probate until June 14th, 1886.

Discouraged that Media would not come to settle her mother's estate, Samuel and Katie returned home. There was much to do over the next few days. Joseph and Samuel finished the fences and pens and they moved the horses, cattle, hogs, and chickens back to the Haskin homestead. Once the livestock was moved, they began planting. After the potatoes and cane were planted, the men spent a couple more days building fences before they began planting the corn.

On June 13th, Katie and Samuel took off for Neligh. They spent the night on the banks of the Elkhorn River west of town. When they appeared in court the next day, they found they were the only ones present to probate Julia's estate. Media still refused to appear. Samuel suspected that Media had no intention of coming to settle her mother's affairs. Therefore, he devised a plan. Since Media was not present to prove on Julia's will of April 14th, Samuel asked that the will of December 26th, 1885 be entered for probate. In that particular document, Julia gave all the real and personal property to Samuel Haskin. The Judge entered Samuel's request and scheduled the next hearing for probate on July 12th.

"Sam," Katie enquired, "what are you doing?"

"I've known Media since she was a little girl," Samuel

answered. "I'm just giving her a little bait. After all, you'll never catch a fish without bait."

Katie looked at him, puzzled. However, he offered no more explanation, instead, he simply urged his horses toward home.

On June 22nd, the County Superintendent returned to the settlement of Mars. He told Samuel that since the community now had a post office, the school could be returned. Samuel could not have been more pleased. However, the County Superintendent told him that the district was to be divided in two. One district would serve the Knox County students, while the other would serve those in Antelope County. The Knox County School would be named the Verdigris Creek School and construction of the schoolhouse was already underway. The schoolhouse in Knox County was located a little over a mile to the north and east of Mars.

On June 27th, Samuel went to the home of Andrew Jones at Walnut Grove, hoping to speak with John Brown's widow, Charlotte, who was working there to pay off John's debt. When John Brown died, he owed some money to some of his neighbors. For the past two years, Charlotte and her sons were trying to wipe the slate clean. Robert Brown was currently working for A. E. Adams and Peter Brown was working for his brother-in-law, John Strope. As Samuel's buckboard pulled up to the Jones house, Andrew came to the door. "Come on in for some coffee," he said to Samuel.

As the men drank their coffee, Samuel told Andrew that he intended to ask Charlotte Brown for her hand in marriage. Samuel had admired Charlotte for some time and had intended to ask for her hand after he divorced Elizabeth. However, Julia became ill and required his assistance. He told Andrew that Julia's affairs would soon be settled and he would be free to ask for Charlotte's hand.

"If Charlotte is agreeable to this arrangement, I will pay off the balance of her debt to you," Samuel told Andrew.

Andrew called Charlotte in from the back yard and Samuel explained to her his intentions. While Charlotte had known Samuel for most of her life, she had never thought of him as anything more than a close friend. She was going to have to give this proposition some thought. In the meantime, with Andrew's permission, she agreed to spend a couple days with Samuel at Mars.

The next morning, Samuel again asked for Mrs. Brown's hand in marriage in exchange for paying of her husband's debt to Andrew Jones. Charlotte declined the offer and made a counter offer. "Pay the debt to Andrew Jones," she began, "as well as the debt to Mr. Adams and the debt to my son-in-law, John Strope, and then I will agree to marry you."

Samuel was impressed. Charlotte Brown was a strong woman with a good head on her shoulders. She would make him a good wife. "I accept your offer," he told her.

Charlotte stayed with Samuel and Katie for four days. While there, she cleaned, cooked, and sewed. She made Samuel a pair of pants and was about to mend one of his shirts when the sewing machine broke. Unable to fix the machine, Samuel sent for Mary Brandt, who had been coming frequently to sew some clothes for her little girl. After Mary arrived, she had the sewing machine running in no time at all.

Early in the morning, on June 30th, Samuel took Charlotte back to Walnut Grove. He expected Julia's estate to be settled on July 12th and Charlotte told him that she would go to Neligh with him for the hearing. Once the estate was settled, they would go to Niobrara to get married.

The day before Independence Day, Julius Hering of Jessup put on a big celebration. All the settlers for miles around were expected at the festivities. Samuel, Katie, and Katie's daughter, Mary Ellen, intended to spend a quiet day with the Wallis Haskin family. However, Wallis and his family decided at the last minute to go to Jessup for the big celebration. Wallis asked his father if he wanted to go with them, but Samuel did not wish to go. Mary Ellen, on the other hand, begged her mother and Katie let her go with Wallis.

Samuel and Katie went back to the boarding house. As Katie was fixing dinner, Louis Morsett came running into the house, shaking and out of breath. Samuel was surprised to see him. He thought that Louis would take his family to Jessup for the celebration. Samuel asked him to sit down, but Louis shook his head.

"What's wrong?" Samuel asked.

"Joseph is dead," he replied. "My son, Joseph, is dead."

Samuel nearly fell to the floor in shock. Joseph Morsett could be no more than seven years old. How could he be dead? Samuel asked Louis what had happened. The Frenchman told him that he had asked his daughter Jeanette to harness the oxen so they could go the July 4th celebration. Sixteen-year old Jeanette and seven-year old Joseph took their two-year old brother, Charley, out to the pasture to get the oxen. Before they arrived where the oxen were grazing, Jeanette told Joseph that she needed to stop to rest. Being anxious to get to the celebration, Joseph told his sister that he would harness the oxen and bring them back. He went on ahead while Jeanette and Charley rested in the shade of the big oak tree at the edge of the pasture.

After several minutes, when Joseph did not return with the oxen, Jeanette told Charley to stay put, while she went to see what was taking so long. As she reached the top of the hill, she sensed that something was wrong. She saw that the oxen were harnessed, but it appeared as if Joseph was lying in the grass behind them. She called to her brother, and receiving no answer, she ran down the hill. As she drew closer, she again called out Joseph's name, but he made no sound and he did not move. She ran to Joseph's side and turned over his limp and bloody body. Her little brother was dead. Looking around, she saw that Joseph had been drug over a tree stump. Something must have spooked the oxen just as he finished harnessing them. As they bolted, he must have kept holding on to the reigns in hopes of stopping them.

Sickened by the gruesome sight and crying, she picked up Joseph's broken body and carried him back to the tree where Charley sat patiently waiting. She told Charley to follow her as she carried her dead brother back to their house.

Samuel put his head into his hands. What could he say? There was nothing he could do or say that would ease his friend's pain. He knew that Cyrus Carver would be over to Jessup and that Louis would need to have a casket prepared for his son. He told the Frenchman to go on home to his family. Meanwhile, Samuel rode to Jessup to get Cyrus.

The fourth of July was supposed to be a day of merriment and joyous celebration. However, throughout the hills of Mars, there was no happiness. For today, the people of Mars were not only burying one of their own, they were burying a small boy. They mourned for a lifetime much too short and a future that would never come. The death of any child was never easy to understand. It was not fair, but then, what in life is? Once again, a crowd gathered on the lonely little hill where a growing number of their friends and neighbors lie in eternal sleep. Once more, a pine box was carefully lowered into a sandy hole. Even the hill, which overlooked the brownish, green river below, seemed to weep over this senseless death.

Mother Nature, herself, seemed to be protesting the loss of this child. Although she had no tears to shed, she relentlessly beat upon the prairies with hot, dry winds. Samuel and Joseph Kibbee labored to save the corn. As Samuel harvested the rye, Joseph would pile the straw around the withering cornstalks in hopes of keeping the winds from sucking the last vestige of water from the parched soil. When they finished with the rye and corn, the two weary men turned their attention to the barley and cane. What little barley they cut, was hauled to the mill. Because of the dry weather, the cane had not yet poked up through the ground, so Samuel plowed the furrows to loosen and turn the soil.

As the sun rose during the early hours of July 12th,

Samuel, Katie, and Charlotte were on their way to Neligh. Samuel hoped that his tactic of asking for the probate of Julia's first will would bring Media. When they arrived at the courthouse, he was not disappointed. Media was there.

When asked by the court, Samuel agreed to have Julia's first will dismissed. Then, he requested probate of Julia's second will and codicil thereof. The court granted Julia's homestead, her household possessions, and her land in Minnesota to her daughter, Media Brill. Samuel agreed to pay all of Julia's medical bills and the funeral expense in exchange for the house and the granary, both of which set on his deceased wife's homestead.

Edwin Haskin's Wife, Delia
Haskin Family Photo.

Chapter 11 The Trouble With Kate

Julia's estate was finally settled. It had been a long ten months, but at least her final wishes were granted. On July 14th, Samuel paid the debts that were owed by John Brown when he was killed, thereby freeing Charlotte and her two sons from their bonds. Then, he and Charlotte went to Niobrara and were wed by nightfall.

When they returned from Niobrara the next day, they rearranged the store to accommodate the eatery, which they moved from Julia's boarding house. Next, Charlotte selected a location about a half a mile to the south where they would build their new house. It was a lovely spot on a hill, which overlooked the river and was within shouting distance of the Cyrus Carver place.

Finally on the July 22nd, the rains came. It began raining in the afternoon and continued through the night. The crops soaked up the moisture like sponges and, in a mere twenty-four hours, the corn seemed to grow a foot. The cane shot through the soil and reached out for the sky.

Samuel began working on his new house. After digging the cellar, he then moved the granary from Julia's place and then headed to Creighton for the lumber. With the help of his two sons and Joseph Kibbee, it was not long until the frame of the house was up. Within days, the roof was finished and most of the siding was nailed into place.

On September 13th, the County Superintendent returned to Mars and selected the spot for the schoolhouse. The site he chose was the exact spot they had moved the log schoolhouse from only a few months earlier. Samuel told him that the log house would not be moved back. Instead, they had another house in mind that was closer which they could move to the location he had chosen. Samuel took the Superintendent to the former boarding house. After examining the building, the Superintendent gave Samuel his approval. A lease would be drawn up and Samuel would be notified when it was ready for his signature.

During the end of September, the folks of Mars began to harvest their crops. Wheat, oats, rye, and barley were hauled to the mill, corn was picked, and cane was made into molasses. Most of the crops were out by the first part of October and Samuel had some time to work on the chimney for his new house. The nights were beginning to get colder and the fireplace and chimney would need to be finished before he and Charlotte could move in.

Samuel received word by the middle of October that the school lease was ready for his signature. On October 12th, he signed the lease and, the next day, Julia's boarding house was moved to the flat area west of the general store. Samuel and Wallis, with the help of George Taylor and Joseph Kibbee, used three teams of horses to move the building to its new spot. Within a week, the fall term began and the new schoolhouse was full of pupils.

By the end of October, Samuel, Charlotte, Katie, and Mary Ellen moved into their new house on the hill. Now that Katie and her daughter were living at Mars, she had become very popular with all the young bachelors. Rarely did a night go by that Katie did not have a gentleman caller. Samuel spoke with her about settling down with one of the young men, but Katie told him that she just was not ready for matrimony. Samuel was not going to push her. She had done well for herself and her daughter, so she knew what was best.

Katie's most frequent caller was an older man named George VanOstrand. George was in his mid forties and at least 15 years older than Katie's other suitors. George, who had lost his first wife in 1880, was introduced to Katie by his son, Jeremiah, who was in the area working on some bridges during the middle of October. Shortly after the two were introduced, George moved from Neligh to a farm at Pleasant Valley.

Almost daily, VanOstrand took his evening meal with the young housekeeper. It was apparent that he was beginning to develop deep feelings for her. While Katie was friendly with him, she did not view him as anything more than just a friend. Carefully, she made sure that she neither did nor said anything that would give him the impression that she was returning his affections. More than once, she voiced her concerns to Samuel and Charlotte.

At the end of October, George VanOstrand asked Katie if she would help him with some housework for a couple days. She agreed. However, after three days, she found that he really wanted her for more than housekeeping, and she demanded that he return her to her home. When she returned to Mars, she told Samuel and Charlotte what had happened and told them that she did not want to see Mr. VanOstrand again.

When George returned on November 5th to get Katie, Samuel told him that she could not go. George was not about to take no for an answer. As he went to enter the house, he found the door blocked by all 6 foot and 260 pounds of Samuel Haskin. George, himself, was considered a big man, but Samuel was even bigger. For just a brief instant, he entertained the notion of forcing his way past the older, larger man who was blocking his entry. However, he soon dismissed the thought, walked back to his buckboard, and drove off to the west.

When Samuel turned around to enter his house, he nearly walked over Katie. He could see that she was very upset and she was shaking in fear.

"You know he'll be back," she said.

"If you don't want to go with him," Samuel told her, "I won't let him take you."

Two days later, Mr. VanOstrand returned. Samuel was about to confront him, but Katie told him that it was no use. He would keep coming no matter how many times he was sent away. Yes, he would keep coming and eventually someone would get hurt, or worse. Therefore, Katie agreed to go with him. Samuel attempted to change her mind, but to no avail. Leaving her daughter with Samuel and Charlotte, she left with VanOstrand.

The next day, Katie came walking back to Mars. As she

walked into the house, she told Samuel that she needed to speak with Charlotte. Knowing it would be woman talk, Samuel set out to the granary to husk corn.

When George VanOstrand arrived the next morning, Katie packed her clothes, packed her daughter's things, and placed them in his buckboard. She turned to Samuel with a smile. "It's alright, Sam," she said. "I'll be keeping house for him."

With a lump in his throat, Samuel told her, "If you need anything, anything at all."

Katie interrupted him. "I know." George helped her and Mary Ellen into the buckboard and they drove off to the west.

As the wagon rolled down the trail and out of sight, Charlotte walked up behind Samuel and placed her hand firmly on his shoulder. "Sam, it's her decision."

Samuel looked to his wife and smiled. He knew that Charlotte was right and that Katie would be fine. Still, he was going to miss her.

Katie's leaving, brought back painful memories for him. The loss of Raviah and the loss of Annie weighed heavy on his very soul. Daily he visited Annie's grave in the hopes of finding some comfort there. Finding neither relief nor comfort from the ghosts of his daughter and wife, he busied himself fixing up his new home. If he kept himself busy, Samuel found that he could keep from feeling sorry for himself.

One evening after a long day's labor, as Samuel and Charlotte finished their supper, they heard a commotion from the calf pen north of their house. Running to the door Samuel saw three dogs converging on one of the calves.

"Charlotte," he shouted. "Bring my rifle."

Charlotte emerged from the house carrying Samuel's gun. A gunshot pierced the air amidst the noise and commotion of the barking and bawling. As one dog fell to the hard ground, its companions in crime wasted no time removing themselves from the scene.

Samuel and Charlotte ran to the pen. The calf, although

suffering several bite wounds, was still alive. Samuel bent over to look at the intruder. His shot was true, the bullet entered in front of the left ear and out the other side of the skull. More than likely, the dog was dead before it even hit the ground. As Samuel inspected the dog, he recognized it as belonging to Charles Joerissen.

As Charlotte tended to the wounded calf, Samuel loaded the dog into his wagon, hitched a horse, and drove to the Joerissen cabin. Charles came out of the cabin as he heard the wagon approach. As Samuel jumped down from the wagon, he noticed that the other two dogs were around the corner of the cabin seemingly hiding as if they knew they had committed a capital crime.

"What's wrong, Sam?" Charles asked.

"Your dogs paid me a visit this evening. They chewed up one of Charlotte's calves pretty bad. I shot one of 'em."

Charles walked over to the wagon and looked at the dead dog in the back. Sure enough, it was one of his.

Charles walked to the cabin and retrieved his rifle. "We can't have a dog around that's goin' to kill calves," he told Samuel. "I'll take care of the other two."

Just then, Joerissen's foster daughter, Emma stepped to the door. She overheard what her foster father told Samuel. "No, you can't," she screamed, tears running down her cheeks.

Charles turned to his ten-year old girl, "Sorry, my dear. But, it just has got to be done."

Crying, Emma ran into the cabin. Samuel looked at Charles. "Perhaps," Samuel began to say.

"No, Sam," Charles said sadly. "If they killed once, they'll surely kill again. We'll talk to Emma."

"She's a might young to understand," stated Samuel.

Samuel knew that there was nothing more that could be done and, that evening, Charles did what he had to. Samuel felt for little Emma and he felt responsible. However, he knew there was nothing else that he or Charles could do. The dogs had the taste of blood and, if they had not been destroyed, they would have kept on terrorizing the neighbors' cattle.

After a mid-November snow storm, the weather warmed up and Samuel put up his well house. Then on November 26th, Kate and Mary Ellen came for a visit. She told Samuel and Charlotte that George was good to both her and her daughter. However, she missed living at Mars. Katie and her daughter stayed until evening, and then headed back to Pleasant Valley.

At the end of November, Charlotte's sixteen-year-old son, Peter, came for a visit. He was a handsome young man of slender build with dark brown hair. Peter was living with his sister Harriet and her husband, John Strope. He was working for John in exchange for room and board. Samuel knew that Charlotte missed her children and Peter was wanting to go to school. The Stropes were very good to him, but there was no time for schooling. Since Katie was now living at Pleasant Valley with George VanOstrand, the Haskins had extra room, so Samuel suggested that Peter move in with them.

"You'll have to work here, too," Samuel told him. "But, you'll have time to go to school, if you want."

Peter was thrilled. "Mr. Haskin, I don't know what to say. Thanks." He shook Samuel's hand then hugged his mother.

On December 5th, Peter moved in with his mother and Samuel. A couple days later, he started school. He had attended school before his father died, then he was forced to work in order to pay off debts and had to drop out. Being able to go back to school was almost like a dream. He had to pinch himself to make sure he was awake. It was not a dream; it was real and he was very thankful to Samuel for giving him the chance to pursue his education.

Joseph Kibbee arrived for work just as Peter was heading off to school. "Where you going?" Joseph asked jokingly. "Weren't you suppose to help us cut wood today?"

Peter knew that Joseph was just giving him a hard time. "Nope, figured you could use the exercise today. So, I guess I'll let you do it all."

When Joseph entered the house, Samuel and Charlotte

were eating breakfast. "Want some breakfast?" Samuel asked him.

"Naw, thanks anyway. Sylvia put up some good doin's this mornin'. I couldn't eat another bite."

Joseph's wife, Sylvia was a good cook. Samuel was glad that Joseph found himself a good wife.

"Joe," Samuel said as he reached for the tobacco pouch in his shirt pocket. "How would you like a little trip to Pleasant Valley today?"

"Sure," he replied. "What's up?"

"I need you to go up to VanOstrand's and talk to Kate about her share of the crops and livestock. If she's goin' to stay there, she needs to come and get her stuff. Take Sylvia with you, then you can go on and see your family at Glenalpine."

Samuel spent the day cutting wood and then the next day, he went to the mill. He purchased a pair of overalls as a Christmas present for Joseph. While he was at the mill, he had a nice visit with his old friend, Julius Hering. The people of Jessup were still awaiting the construction of the railroad. The surveyors had once again been through the area just a month before, and it now appeared certain that construction would start soon.

The next day, VanOstrand and Katie came for some of Kate's chickens. Kate's brother George Goodman was with them. Samuel wondered when they would be coming for the rest of Kate's stuff. Katie told him that she would be back the next day. However, she only took the rest of her chickens when she returned, but left the rest of her livestock.

Samuel was furious. Was she expecting him to feed and care for her livestock for nothing? Plus, she had some grain that he was storing for free. On December 13th, Samuel paid a visit to Kate. She did not seem to be in any hurry to get her hogs, cattle, and grain, so Samuel told her that he was going to have to start charging her for keeping her livestock. That did not set well with her and an argument ensued. Samuel was a hard man to anger, but after his experience with Elizabeth, he was not about to be taken advantage of again. He stood his ground and gave Katie seven days to remove her animals and grain.

The next day, VanOstrand and George Goodman came for Kate's hogs and cattle. Then, on December 20th, Kate and George Goodman returned for the wheat, oats, rye, and barley. Samuel tried to talk to her, but she did not wish to speak to him. Watching as the Goodman's drove off toward Pleasant Valley, Samuel could not help but feel that he had lost more than a friend. He only wanted the best for her and now it seemed that she resented him for that. For a while, after she had come into his life, it seemed almost as if she had replaced his long lost daughter. Now, as he watched the wagon roll over the hills to the west, he felt as if he was losing Raviah all over again.

The cold north wind howled through the trees and the waves rippled through the brownish, green waters of the Verdigris. A coyote's howl echoed through the hills as Samuel pulled the collar of his coat up around his neck. "Good bye Katie," he said as he turned and walked toward his house.

Chapter 12   The Blizzard

"On January 12, 1888, the weather was so nice, being such a warm spring like morning. About 11 o'clock it started to rain, but by 3 o'clock we were having a blizzard, with lots of fine snow and strong wind blowing, and it kept getting colder and colder. My two older sisters and I and two neighbor boys started for home, going as fast as we could."

"My sisters had a lunch pail with just a cloth tucked into it for a cover, and that cloth blew out and was lost. The girls wanted to go back and see if they could find it, but the neighbor boys, really young men 18 or 20 years old, would not let them go back. So we went on for home. About the last forty rods of the way, they saw that I was freezing, so the boys told my sisters to follow as fast as they could because they were going to try to get me to the house. They each took me by the hand and started on the run. I remembered when we crossed the creek on the ice, but we still had half of the way to go. I don't know how we got that last twenty rods. The next thing I knew, I was in the house with my feet and hands packed in snow, and snow was also packed on my face and ears. I got thawed out and was no worse for the experience. If it had not been for those two neighbor boys, neither my sisters nor I would have gotten home."

> From *"Events in the Life of Elmer F. Haskin"*
> As dictated to his daughter Helene B. Hansen
> In 1965

There is nothing quite like a dance at the Shib Carver place to help bring in a new year. Music and drink along with much laughter and food was guaranteed at one of Shib's dances. The festivities lasted well into the night and on into the next morning. By sunrise, the last of Shib's guests were on their way home. Although it was custom for the Carvers to host most of the dances during the long winter months, this dance was special. Shib announced his upcoming marriage to the widow,

Meyer. The widow had moved with her family to Knox County, Nebraska in 1879. Then in 1884, her husband became sick with fever, which claimed his life. The Meyers had but one child, a little girl named Della, who was now ten years old. Shib and the widow Meyer would be wed on January 13th and everyone was invited back to celebrate.

The snow in the morning of the 13th did little to dampen the spirits of the residents of Mars. By noon, a linen blanket of white covered the rolling hills as if they were specially decked for the occasion. Shib and the widow Meyer were married early in the afternoon. Then in the evening, fiddle players briskly worked their wonder. Couples, young and old, moved and countered to the lively beat.

If only for a brief moment, cares were left behind. Nevertheless, morning dawned once again, and with it came the reality of the labors required for basic survival. Snows and thaws, like the ebbs and tides, repeated their cycles through the dark days of winter at Mars. However, darkness soon yields to the dawn, so winter gives way for the springing forth of new life. Thus, even with the longer days and warmer temperatures, the cycle continues. Plowing the soil and planting the seed, the farmers toiled. The changing of season brought only a shift in the labor. Abundant rains meant abundant harvests and there seemed not a care in the world.

Samuel and Charlotte were now comfortably settled into their new three-room, wood-frame house. Many evenings found the Haskins lounging on the north side of their home enjoying the sights and sounds of the abundant wildlife in the valley below them. Most summer nights, as the sun disappeared over the western hill, the last thing it saw was Samuel puffing on his pipe with Charlotte sitting at his side, carefully knitting a shawl or blanket.

With the dawn of a new day, Samuel would make his way up to the county line to his little store. Soon, Charlotte would come and fix breakfast for their customers. John Downs, Joe Kibbee, the Fayes, and George Taylor were regulars for the morning meal. Sometimes, even the Carvers or perhaps Andrew Jones stopped in.

Recently, Samuel noticed that he was not moving as fast as he once had. Nor was he able to do as much in a day as he had before. At 67 years old, he was beginning to feel the heavy hand of time. These days, it seemed that he relied more on Charlotte and Joseph than he had in the past. Even still, it seemed as if the work was never done. For the first time in his life, he felt completely overwhelmed by the tasks that lay ahead of him. He began to feel as if the store, the stables, the crops, and the hay were more than he could handle. Charlotte urged him to cut back, but the thought of giving up even one of his responsibilities made him feel like he was placing one foot into his own grave. No, he must push on. He had to. Keeping himself busy kept him from dwelling on the pains of the past.

However, the pains of the past have their way of sneaking up on a person in cruel ways. On August 21st, Ed Haskin came with bad news. His wife, Delia was dead. For years, she had not been well. Several times before, she stood on the edge of the Great Beyond. Somehow, she pulled through when it seemed that all was hopeless. However, each bout left her frail body even weaker. Only shear will power, fueled by her love for her five children, kept her going. But, death was not to be cheated. Neither will power nor love could stay the reaper indefinitely.

Two of Ed and Delia's children, Spencer and Anna, were now grown. Spencer was nearly 22 years old and Anna was 18 and married. However, the younger children ranged in age from nine to thirteen and still needed their mother. Ed's mail route kept him away from home much of the time and life had not been easy for his family. Now, with Delia gone, their children had an uncertain future.

Once more Samuel felt the old wound open wide. The ghosts of Raviah and Annie tortured his soul. What was the purpose? Why had he been put on this earth? Was it only to suffer one loss after another? Where would it end? So many unanswered questions plagued his thoughts. Just when he thought he had found peace, he turned around to find only emptiness.

Delia's funeral was held in Creighton and she was laid to rest in the Millerboro Cemetery five miles east of Mars. Delia maintained a strong faith in God, even at the very end. Pallbearers lowered the wooden casket into the ground. Many a time, Delia had elegantly eulogized the recently past. Now, Mary Carver spoke words of hope and comfort as the earth exacted its final prize.

With his mother gone, Spencer stayed at his parents' homestead with his younger siblings. Edwin continued his mail route and stayed in Creighton most of the time. Cyrus Carver and Wallis Haskin checked on Edwin's children frequently. Other neighbors also watched out for them. However, Spencer was a capable young man and he provided very well for his sisters and brother.

The harvest during the fall of 1887 was quite possibly the best the settlers of Mars had ever seen. Samuel and Charlotte were not only busy with their own harvest, they were also busy at the store keeping their neighbors supplied with the necessities of life. Meanwhile, Joseph Kibbee worked on new stables south of the Mars Store. By December 1st, Mars could boast an extensive livery stable capable of housing up to sixteen horses. Pens around the old stable were now used for cows and calves.

Everyone at Mars enjoyed weddings, which provided just one more excuse to hold a dance. On New Year's Day, 1888, Maria Sophia Haskin's brother, Charley Brandt married Fannie Burton. Charley met Fannie when she was teaching at the little log schoolhouse on the county line. The wedding took place at Fannie's parents' house near Neligh. After the wedding, everyone returned to the hills of Mars to enjoy music and dance at the Shib Carver place. The Carver dances were sure to warm body and soul, no matter how cold the temperatures.

The cold weather of early January finally broke with

warmer conditions on January 10th, 1888. On the morning of January 12th, the temperatures were well into the upper 50's by nine o'clock in the morning. Being such a fine, spring-like day, many of the children headed off to school wearing only light jackets. A few children went to school without jackets altogether. Meanwhile, some of the farmers headed to Niobrara or Creighton to do some shopping.

At the Mars School, the children played ball during the morning recess. The Mars School teacher, Jennie Sherman, gave her pupils an extra fifteen minutes of play before she rang the school bell. At the Verdigris Creek School, Jennie's sister, Belle, played fox and goose with her pupils during the morning break. The students at both schools suffered from spring fever and found it difficult to concentrate on their schoolwork.

It started to rain by 11:00am. Shortly after the rain began, the winds picked up from the east. By 1:00pm, the winds switched to the north and it began to snow. Within an hour, the winds increased and the temperatures dropped below 30 degrees. The blizzard was in full swing by 3:00pm.

Belle Sherman was about to release her pupils when Charles Gardner came for his children. The storm was so bad that, when Mr. Gardner entered the schoolhouse, his face and beard were completely covered in snow and ice. He advised Belle to hold the students at the school unless their families came for them. Charley Brandt arrived and picked up his little sister, Kate. Corwin Gardner arrived with a team of mules to pick up his three sisters. However, the mules had to face the storm on the way home and Corwin only made it about a half a mile before he had to stop at a neighbor's place to stable his team. Then, he and his sisters returned to the school.

Moses Morrill soon came for his daughters, Margaret and Myrtle. He also picked up the Joerissen's foster daughter, Emma. Moses took Emma to the Dana place and then he dropped his daughters off at his place before he drove down to the county line to let the Joerissens know where Emma was staying. Although he had less than a half a mile to go from the

Joerissen place to his home, he almost did not make it. The wind was in his face making it difficult to breathe. Plus, to make matters worse, Moses could not see because of the fierce wind-driven snow and almost became lost.

Mart Neal and Frank Peregoy arrived at the Verdigris Creek School to pick up their children. However, both sensed that they would not make it back home, so they stayed at the school.

Those who stayed at the school shared bread and cake while Belle placed quilts on the floor by the stove for the younger children to sleep. As night descended upon the valley, Belle lit the coal lamps. The coal bin was attached to the back of the school, so there was an ample supply for both stove and lamps.

The older children and the adults were unable to sleep and passed their time with a spelling match, recitations, and even a debate. When they could think of nothing else to do, they huddled on the floor around the stove.

As the blizzard roared into the Verdigris River valley, Jennie Sherman released her pupils at 4:00pm. Peter Brown took off to the southeast, while Wallis and Maria Sophia's children, Mercedes, Florence, and Elmer, with the help of Bart and Orland Carver, made their way south along the river. They were only a short distance from the school when, all at once, Florence started to go back. Seeing her sister turn around, Mercedes followed her. Bart noticed both girls seemed to be heading back the direction from which they had just came.

"What's going on?" He shouted to the girls.

"A towel blew out of my lunch box," Florence replied. "I need to find it."

Bart shook his head. "Let it go. We have to keep moving."

Florence was about to argue with him when he took her by the arm and pulled her in the direction of home. As he did so, he shouted to Mercedes to follow.

About a quarter of a mile from the school, Orland noticed that Elmer was beginning to slow down. There was still about a half a mile to go and it did not look like Elmer was going to make it. Orland grabbed Elmer by the hand and told Bart to take his other hand. Then he instructed Mercedes and Florence to follow them as fast as they could.

Orland and Bart ran as they had never run before. Shortly after they crossed the river, Elmer lost consciousness. Bart took him in his arms and ran as fast as he could toward the Wallis Haskin cabin. Orland ran back to Mercedes and Florence and helped them the rest of the way home. After the Haskin children were safely home, the Carver boys made their way to the river and were able to follow it to their cabin, which was only a quarter of a mile from the Wallis Haskin place. Despite the short distance, it seemed like a hundred miles to the frozen and exhausted boys. They were thankful when they finally reached home.

When Elmer came to, he was in front of the fireplace and his hands and feet were numb and packed in snow. Maria Sophia was washing his face with a warm washcloth. The snow had caked around his eyes and he even had snow in his ears. Before long, he was completely thawed and eating warm corn meal by the fireplace.

While the Carver boys were rushing Elmer home, Jennie Sherman instructed the rest of her pupils to hold hands and form a chain. She placed the oldest boy at the front of the chain. As she led her chain of children through the valley, she would drop each pupil off as they passed their respective cabins. In this manner, she led each child safely home.

When the blizzard began, Samuel and Charlotte were both at the general store. Charlotte went to tend to the cows in the east stables as Samuel looked to the horses in the south stables. After they saw to their livestock, they met back at the store. Cold and covered in ice and snow, Samuel took Charlotte's hand and they trudged through the furious onslaught of the blizzard toward their house. Their house was a little over a quarter of a mile south of the store and even though the wind was at their backs, they could not see more than ten feet in front of them. The wind-driven snow was decreasing visibility to near zero.

Slowly, Samuel and Charlotte pushed forward. Generally, the walk from the store to their house only took a couple minutes, but they had already been struggling for more than five minutes and they had only traversed half the distance. Just when they came within 50 yards of their house, Samuel slipped and fell to the ground, twisting his ankle in the process, and pulling Charlotte down with him. Between his exhaustion and the piercing pain in his ankle, he was unable to rise.

Charlotte picked herself up and in dismay noticed that Samuel could not get up. She reached down, grabbed his arm, and pulled with all her strength, but Samuel was a very big man and she could not budge him.

Samuel knew that neither one of them would survive much longer. They both were exhausted, cold, and wet. "Go on," Samuel told Charlotte. "Leave me."

"No," she replied as she tugged on his arm. Still, she could not budge him.

"It's no use," Samuel cried. "Go, now!"

Charlotte paid him no heed. She moved around behind her husband and worked him into a sitting position. She then wrapped her arms around him and under his arms. She clasped her hands together at his chest and then with near superhuman effort, she pulled with all her might. Samuel was up, but he nearly went back down as pain shot up his leg. However, Charlotte was prepared. She braced herself and steadied her husband.

"Lean on me," she instructed.

Bearing a large portion of Samuel's weight, somehow Charlotte managed to help him to the house. Once inside, she helped him to a chair. Then, after she started the fire to warm the house, she helped her husband into dry clothes. Samuel's ankle was swollen, but nothing was broke. Both of them felt very fortunate that they made it home safely. Within the hour, Peter Brown came through the door with snow covered eyebrows and ice hanging from his eyelashes.

As the storm hit in the afternoon, Edwin Haskin was half way between Neligh and Mars on his mail route. Edwin carried extra jackets, boots, gloves, and even blankets, so when the temperature dropped, he stopped and put on his heavy jacket and wrapped himself in a blanket. Soon he found that the temperature was the least of his worries. With the fury of the storm, he was unable to see where he was going. Before long, he was uncertain as to which direction he was going.

He thought about turning back toward Neligh, but realized that he did not know which direction that was. For all he knew he was already headed in that direction. If he were still headed toward Mars, he should pass through Royal, which was a settlement nearly six miles south of Mars. If for some reason, he had veered off toward the northeast, then he should eventually come upon Chicago, a small settlement about ten miles southwest of Creighton. Nervously, he strained his eyes in hopes of seeing even a farmstead where he could take refuge. However, he saw nothing.

Slowly and surely, his team plodded onward. The horses kept their heads down and labored forward, always forward. Edwin tried to listen for the beat of the hooves, but he heard nothing. When he would try to look up, the wind would drive the snow into his face with such power that he was forced to look back down at his feet. He was almost certain that they were headed into the wind, but with the way it was gusting, it was very hard to tell. He suspected that the wind was blowing from the north and if he was indeed headed into the wind, then he must still be moving toward Mars. Then the horrible truth dawned on him. He was not even sure that they were moving at all. By the feel of his reins, he thought they were moving, but perhaps it was just the wind that he felt tugging on his reins. For sanity's sake, he kept telling himself that the wagon was moving.

He fought the temptation to crawl off the wagon in order to see if it was still rolling. He knew that if the wagon was moving and he crawled off, he could injure himself or possibly be struck down by one of the wheels. Additionally, if the wagon was not moving and he crawled off, the horses could move ahead before he could stop them. If that were to happen, even if the horses moved only twenty feet ahead, he may never find them in all this blowing snow. Therefore, Edwin decided to stay on the wagon and pray that they were still moving toward a settlement.

Darkness only added to his confusion and he was even uncertain what time it was. It felt like hours upon hours had passed. It seemed an eternity. The cold was beginning to take its toll on both his mind and his body. His fingers and toes began to sting. He kept straining to look forward, but the wind and the snow made it impossible to do so. The wind was blowing the snow so hard that the flakes felt like sharp knives hitting his face. Even glancing side to side was difficult. Still, he kept looking and kept praying for any signs of habitation. No matter how hard he looked, no matter now hard he prayed; he saw nothing except white.

Soon, he began to notice that the wind was not blowing quite as hard. In fact, he almost thought that he could see the backs of his horses. Yes! Yes, he could see his horses and they were moving! He still could not see beyond them because of the wind and the snow, and he was still lost. However, he felt some degree of comfort to know that the horses were still taking him somewhere, even if he did not know where that was.

Several times, he thought that he saw a shadow of a building or a light of a cabin, so he would guide his team toward the apparition and nothing was there. His mind was beginning to play tricks on him. Once again, he started to lose all hope. Just as he was thinking it was hopeless, the horses stopped. He tried to urge them forward but they would not move.

"Well," he said to himself. "This is where I'm goin' to

die."

He was about to lay down on the seat of his wagon when he thought he saw a cabin less than thirty feet on his right. He figured that his mind must have been playing tricks on him again. He shook his head and rubbed his eyes but the apparition did not disappear. Could it be real? Was that really a cabin?

There was only one way to tell for sure. He crawled down from his wagon and stumbled toward the vision. The closer he got, the clearer he saw. It was a cabin! He knocked on the door and tried to shout out, but he could not find his voice. Still, he continued to knock. Then the door opened and standing before him was none other than his brother, Wallis Haskin.

At first, Wallis did not recognize the man at the door. Edwin's beard was full of ice and both of his eyes were nearly frozen closed. He was covered from head to foot in snow. As Wallis reached out to help the man into the house, he saw that it was Edwin.

Maria Sophia saw to her brother-in-law while Wallis un-hitched the horses from the mail wagon and took them to the barn. When Wallis returned to the house, he found Edwin sitting by the fireplace, still trying to remove the ice and snow from his face. It was nearly an hour before Wallis and Maria Sophia were able to remove all the packed snow from Edwin's clothes. Edwin was amazed that the horses brought him to his brother's place. He told Wallis that he had no idea where he was or which direction he had been traveling.

As bad as the blizzard was in the Verdigris River valley, it was many times worse up on the prairies. The hills and the trees that surrounded the river helped to protect the people of Mars from the worst of the storm. There were no deaths at Mars nor any livestock lost. Some of the surrounding settlements did not fair as well. A teacher from Plainview died with three of her pupils, within 200 feet of shelter. In Holt County, a teacher was found dead in a haystack. Many cows, horses, and pigs perished on the prairies above the valley. The blizzard of 1888 was the worst that the settlers of Mars had ever experienced.

After the storm subsided, the people of Mars once again resumed their lives. The wind had blown the snow into great drifts so hard that horses could walk right over them. In the days that followed, there was much difficulty in even the simplest of chores. However, neighbors helped one another and by working together, as they always had, they rose above the hardship caused by nature's fury.

Chapter 13 Murder in the Hills

The blizzard of January 12th was only the beginning. Temperatures plummeted below zero making the short days of winter all the more difficult to bear. February was not much better. For the Haskins, the best thing about February was the birth of Wallis and Maria Sophia's seventh child. They named her Blanche Ellen and she warmed the hearts of all who came to see her.

Soon, the March sun melted the thick icy mantle of winter. Cabin fever stepped aside for the labors of spring and soon the blizzard of 1888 was but a terrible memory to all who survived her. That winter's tales would roll off tongues of children, and their children after them, for many years to come.

Samuel never completely healed from his fall. Even though he now used a cane to walk and his movements were slow and deliberate, he continued to do what he could on the farm. Joseph Kibbee and Peter Brown took care of the tasks and jobs that Samuel could no longer perform. Both boys were like sons to Samuel. Peter finished his schooling by January 1889 and began to manage the pastures and the stables. Joseph, who had worked for Samuel for nearly ten years, took care of the fields and gardens.

Joseph lived less than a mile north of the Haskin Homestead. He and his wife Sylvia had two little girls, Sylvia Belle, who was four years old and Alta May, who was two. Sylvia brought the girls to the store daily to see Samuel and Charlotte. Samuel always had a treat for the little girls. Charlotte was certain that the old man was going to spoil them rotten.

In March, the Carvers held a big party to honor the marriage of Cyrus' son, Bart, to William Sherman's daughter, Happy Jo. Hundreds of people were present and the celebration continued to almost dawn of the following day.

In September 1889, Joseph Kibbee told Sam and Charlotte that he and Sylvia were going to have another baby.

Charlotte could not tell whether Joseph or Samuel was the most excited.

"If the baby is a boy," Samuel told Joseph, as he took a couple puffs on his pipe, "you better name him Samuel."

"The hell I will," Joseph teased. "I don't want him growin' up to be an old fart like you."

It was the same old story day after day, Samuel and Joseph arguing over the name of the baby. Charlotte thought that Joseph would name the baby "Samuel" even if it were a girl, just to spite her husband. Listening to the two men argue, a stranger would probably think that they did not like one another. However, nothing could be further from the truth. In fact, their relationship was as close as father and son. Losing his own father in 1880, Joseph began turning to Samuel for guidance and advice.

In mid October, Joseph told Samuel that he was very concerned about his little brother. Frank was only 12 years old when their father died and lacked his father's guidance during the time in his life when he needed it the most.

"Something's goin' on," Joseph told Samuel.

"What makes you think that?" Samuel inquired.

"Mother says that he leaves late at night and then does not come back until early morning."

"Have you talked to him?"

"I've tried," Joseph replied, "but he won't tell me a thing."

Even though Samuel advised him to be patient and understanding, Joseph felt he needed to know what Frank was doing. That evening he watched his mother's house from behind a shed, waiting for Frank to leave. Shortly after midnight, he saw his younger brother sneak out of the house. Quietly, Frank saddled a horse then rode off to the northeast. Joseph hurried back to his horse, that he left near a grove of trees almost half a mile south of the house, and then followed his brother's trail.

In the moonlight, Joseph could easily see the fresh hoof marks on the sandy dirt road. He was surprised to see that his brother seemed to be riding toward Mars. Soon he reached a fork in the road. The right road wound its way east to Mars and the left one ran over the hills to the north of the settlement. Frank's tracks led to the north.

As he continued following the trail north, it was not long until he could hear some voices in the distance. He guided his horse off the road and circled around to the west. Safely out of sight of whoever was up ahead, Joseph tied his horse to a tree and carefully moved toward the spot where he heard the voices. Soon he came upon a clearing and saw his brother speaking to a tall middle-aged man. He recognized the older man as Jerome Sharpe, who was a farmer that lived about a mile west of him and Sylvia.

In the moonlight, he saw Jerome hand Frank something that looked like money. Then, Jerome mounted his horse and rode off toward the Sharpe farm, while Frank rode off to the east. Joseph ran back to his horse and once again followed his brother. However, when Frank crossed the Verdigris River, Joseph lost his trail. Although he searched the banks for almost an hour, he was unable to find where his brother left the water.

Next, Joseph rode past his own place, but saw no sign that Frank had been there either. Then the older Kibbee rode to the south past the Mars store and stables. Still, there was no sign of Frank. He then decided to ride back toward the Sharpe farm. Shortly after he crossed the river, he heard several horses approaching rapidly from behind.

Guiding his mount into the shadows at the left of the road, he saw Frank ride past him, leading three horses. Joseph followed him from a safe distance so he would not be seen. Frank took the three horses to a deep canyon on the Sharpe farm. At the end of the canyon, Joseph saw what seemed to be a pen or corral. The younger Kibbee released the three horses into the corral and then rode toward the entrance of the canyon.

Just as Frank came out of the canyon, Joseph rode directly into his path.

"What the hell you doing?" Joseph demanded.

161

Startled, Frank turned his horse back into the canyon only to have his older brother ride up beside him and pull him from his saddle. The younger Kibbee fell to the ground, landing flat on his back. Before he could rise, Joseph jumped onto his chest and pinned his arms to the ground above his head.

"I'll ask you one more time," Joseph said. "What the hell are you doing?"

"Get off me!" screamed Frank.

"When you tell me what you're up to."

"All right! All right, I'll tell you. Just get off me."

Joseph let his little brother up.

"I've been working for Mr. Sharpe," Frank explained in a rather bitter tone. "I've just been trying to get some extra money. Mr. Sharpe pays me to do odd jobs."

"Why so late at night?" Joseph asked.

"I can't during the day, idiot. I have our farm to take care of."

"What about those horses?" Joseph questioned.

"Mr. Sharpe arranged for me to buy them from some man over east."

Joseph still was not satisfied. "What was that man's name?"

"I didn't ask. I just went where he told me and bought the horses."

Joseph had a feeling that his brother was not telling him the truth. He wanted to believe him, but he just had an uneasy feeling about the whole thing. "Go home," he told Frank. "We'll talk about this later."

The next day Joseph told Samuel what had happened. "What do you think, Sam?" Joseph valued Samuel's opinion.

"Does he have a history of lying?" Samuel asked.

"He's always been a little on the wild side. But, I don't think he's ever lied to me before."

Samuel told him to give his brother the benefit of the doubt, at least until he had reason to believe otherwise. Joseph figured that Samuel was right. Perhaps he had been too hard on his younger brother. Anyway, Samuel had made him feel a little better.

Later that day, George Goodman came to the store and told them that three horses had been stolen from a farm near Millerboro. Once again, Joseph became suspicious of his brother. Why would Frank lie to him? Was he in some kind of trouble? Joseph was concerned and once again approached Frank. Still, Frank maintained that he was just doing some odd jobs for Jerome Sharpe and that he had purchased the horses that Joseph saw him with the night before.

Two nights later, some more horses were stolen from another farm near Millerboro. Joseph learned from his mother that Frank had left the cabin that night, too. When Joseph arrived at the Mars Store the next morning, he was going to tell Samuel what his mother said. However, as he walked through the door, he saw that Jerome Sharpe was there with several other men.

"Doc Middleton has been seen between here and Millerboro," Jerome said. "We need to do something about it."

"We'll let the Sheriff know," Wallis Haskin said.

"No, we need to do something about it now," Jerome urged the men.

"Wallis is right," Samuel told the men. "Wallis will let the Sheriff know and we'll let him handle it. Now you all go back to your farms and keep a close watch on your own until we get this settled."

As Joseph left the store to go to the granary to husk some corn, he overheard Jerome telling the other men to round up their neighbors. Sharpe told them to meet him at the Mars Schoolhouse that night. Now, Joseph was really concerned because he felt that Frank had been stealing the horses, and it appeared as if Jerome was going to lay a trap.

Shortly after dark that evening, men from around the area converged on the Mars School. Inside, Jerome Sharpe was organizing a vigilante group to round up Doc Middleton and his gang. When Joseph Kibbee walked through the door, there was no doubt in his mind what was happening. Jerome was inciting a lynch mob and Frank was the one they were going to string up.

"You son of a bitch," Joseph screamed at Jerome. "You know damn well Doc Middleton isn't stealin' the horses."

"Get your ass out of here, kid," Jerome instructed Joseph. "This is man's work."

"Tell them about the horses you've been getting late at night, you thievin' bastard," countered Joseph.

"I don't know what you're talking about, boy," Jerome said angrily. "But, either you walk out of here on your own or we'll throw you out. Makes no difference to me."

Joseph saw that Jerome had the other men so worked up that they were not about to listen to him. He needed to go warn his brother so he slowly backed out of the school. As he mounted his horse, he knew he should go tell Sam Haskin, but there was no time. He had to get to his brother before that lynch mob did. Rapidly, he rode off to the west.

When he arrived at his mother's place, Frank was gone. His mother sensed that something was seriously wrong. Not wanting to worry her, he did not tell her what he suspected. He wasted no time as he galloped toward the canyon on Jerome's farm.

When he reached the corral, he saw that it was empty. He turned his horse around and rode back the way he came. Joseph rode east after he left the canyon. He knew now that he needed Samuel and Wallis to help him. Just as he was about to cross the creek, he saw Frank riding toward him leading two horses.

"Frank," he shouted to his younger brother. "Jerome Sharpe has organized a vigilante group to catch the horse thief. If those horses you have there are stolen, you need to get away from them now. Go home. Stay there. I'm goin' to get Wallis and Samuel to help me stop Jerome."

Before Frank could respond, Joseph rode off to the east. Frank was about to drop the rope and release the two horses, then he seemed to change his mind. Instead of releasing the two horses and going home, he led them into the river. From there he led them rapidly north, staying in the water for nearly eight miles. As soon as they were out of the water, he and his horses continued their journey northward.

Just as Joseph approached Mars, Will Fields rode up to meet him. Will was one of Jerome's hired men and was very well respected in the valley. He handed Joseph a note from Jerome and then rode off to the west. Joseph opened the note.

"Joe, come to my place tonight," the note read. "I wish to apologize for my comments earlier. I'll meet you in front of my granary at midnight. Jerome."

Joseph figured that it had to be getting close to midnight already. He would not have time to get Samuel and Wallis if he were going to meet Jerome on time. Joseph was always punctual. He hated it when people said they would be somewhere at a certain time and then show up late. However, he needed to let his wife know that he was going to be gone for a while. Since his place was on the way to the Sharpe farm anyway, he would not lose any time.

Riding north over the hills, he reached his house just before midnight. Rushing into the house, he found his wife was still awake. He told her that he was going to ride over to the Sharpe place to speak with Jerome and then he was going to ride back to Mars to get Samuel's help with a problem.

"Don't wait up for me," he told Sylvia. Then he gave her a kiss and hurried to the door.

Sylvia ran to the door and watched as her husband rode off to the west. She knew that he was concerned about Frank and hoped that he was not in over his head. As Joseph's horse disappeared over the western hill, Sylvia prayed for his safety.

About five minutes after midnight, Joseph pulled his horse up to the Sharpe granary. He looked around but saw no sign of Jerome. As he jumped from his saddle, he thought he heard a sound from inside the grain bin. Slowly, he approached, opened the door, and then walked inside.

Charlotte Haskin was having a pleasant dream when all at once a knock at the door brought her abruptly from her slumber. Looking around, she saw that it was still dark. Who could be knocking at the door at this hour? She reached over and shook her husband.

"What is it?" Samuel asked.

"Someone's at the door," she replied.

Charlotte put on her night coat and rushed to the door, as Samuel got dressed. When she opened the door, she saw Sylvia Kibbee and her two little girls. Sylvia was crying.

"Dear one," Charlotte said. "Come in."

Just as Sylvia and her girls entered the house, Samuel came out of the bedroom. He saw that Sylvia was very upset over something. "What is it, child?" He asked.

"He's dead," Sylvia cried. Then she buried her head in her hands, sobbing uncontrollably.

Charlotte put her arm around Sylvia and helped her to a chair. Between tears, Sylvia told the Haskins that Joseph had been killed. She said that Jerome Sharpe woke her early to let her know that her husband was dead. According to Jerome, he caught Joseph stealing grain and when Joseph drew his gun, Jerome shot him.

Samuel nearly fell to the floor in shock. No! Not Joseph! It just could not be true. Samuel had known the young Kibbee for ten years and he knew that Joseph would not steal. There must be some mistake. As Charlotte looked after Sylvia and her youngsters, Samuel woke Peter. He told Peter to ride out and get Sylvia's father, William Sherman. As Peter rode to the Sherman place, Samuel hitched his wagon to pick up Wallis.

From the Wallis Haskin homestead, the two Haskin men headed north to the Sharpe place. When they arrived, they found Jerome in his barn. Samuel asked about the shooting and Jerome recounted the events of the prior evening. He told them that he had arranged a meeting of the area farmers at the Mars School and organized groups to search the hills to capture Doc Middleton. As they were about to leave the school, Joseph

166

stormed in and demanded to be a part of the posse. When they refused, he made some threats and then rode off.

Jerome told Sam and Wallis that when he and several of the men returned to the Sharpe farm following their search, they heard a noise inside the granary. When they entered the building, they saw Joseph scooping some grain into a bag. When Joseph saw the men, he pulled his gun and they were forced to shoot him.

"Where's the body?" Samuel asked.

Jerome took the Haskins to the granary where he had laid the body and covered it with a blanket. As Samuel and Wallis inspected the body, they noticed that Joseph had been shot in the back, a fact that they pointed out to Jerome.

"Explain that," Wallis demanded of Jerome.

"I can't," Sharpe replied. "Maybe he turned to hide or something. When we lit our lantern, he was dead, holding on to that bag of grain over there with one hand and his gun in the other."

"If it was dark," Samuel asked, "how is it that you saw him pull a gun?"

"The moon cast enough light," Sharpe answered.

Neither Samuel nor Wallis was satisfied with Jerome's answers, but they could not see a way to prove him wrong. As they walked back outside, Will Fields arrived with the Sheriff. Jerome had sent him to bring the law shortly after the shooting. Once again, Jerome told the events that led to the shooting of Joseph Kibbee. Since the incident appeared to be justified, the Sheriff did not file any charges.

From the Sharpe place, Samuel and Wallis rode to the Lucious Kibbee farm where they told Joseph's mother, Hanna, that her son was dead. She asked them about Frank, but they had not seen him and they were surprised that he was not at home. When Hanna asked her eighteen-year old daughter, Emily, about Frank, she learned that her younger son had left the house late the night before.

Assuring Hanna that they would look for Frank, they

turned their wagon and headed back to the Sharpe farm. They placed Joseph's body in the wagon and took him to Cyrus Carver. Then, Samuel and Wallis split up and asked all the people in the area if anyone had seen the younger Kibbee boy. When they met back at the Mars Store in the afternoon, they still had not found Frank Kibbee. No one had seen or heard anything about him.

On the cold, frosty morning of October 21st, 1889, Joseph Kibbee was laid to rest near his father in the little cemetery on a hill overlooking Mars. After the funeral, the mourners all went their separate ways and only Samuel Haskin remained. For over an hour Samuel stood at the foot of Joseph's grave. He just could not believe that Joseph was gone. His young life cut short so brutally and no one had been brought to justice. Why was it that so many people he loved were taken from him? He prayed long and hard for answers, but no answers came. What was Joseph doing in that grain bin? Where was Frank? How was Sylvia going to survive without her husband?

Then his mind turned to Sylvia. She had two little girls and another baby on the way. That baby would never know its father. Where was the justice in that? Nothing made sense.

The next week, Hanna Kibbee sold her farm. Then she and her daughter along with Sylvia and her girls headed east for Iowa. Hanna had family there and Sylvia just wanted to get away from the cruel and unforgiving hills where her husband was killed. In addition, she figured that Hanna would need her support; and she knew she that needed support from Hanna.

Strangely, the horse stealing stopped after Joseph Kibbee's death and no one had even seen Doc Middleton. A farmer near Niobrara reported seeing a man matching Frank's description crossing the Missouri River, heading north, and leading two horses. Gossip was abundant in the hills and valleys that surrounded Mars. Everyone seemed to have an opinion about the horse thieves and the shooting in the grain bin.

Then, amid the gossip and rumors, another tragedy occurred which spurred even further speculation of foul play.

Will Fields was shot to death behind the Jessup Store. He and his friend, Bert Lockwood, stopped at the store to purchase some ammunition. Several minutes after they made their purchase, Pete O'Malley heard a shot from behind the building. When he arrived on the scene, he saw Fields slumped over in the front of the wagon and Lockwood was holding a rifle. Lockwood told Pete that he was handing the rifle to Fields in the wagon when it accidentally discharged. The bullet hit Fields in the chest but did not kill him.

Pete helped move Fields into the back of the wagon and then the men packed the wound with a towel before rushing the injured man to the doctor at Millerboro. However, Millerboro was seven miles away, and Fields died before they could reach their destination.

Since Jerome Sharpe had fired Fields the day after Joseph Kibbee was killed, folks around Mars were saying that Will was shot deliberately. The talk was that Fields had overheard something he was not supposed to hear and he needed to be eliminated. Whether it was because of rumors or because of guilt over shooting his best friend, Bert Lockwood left the hills of Mars to work in Norfolk. However, after two weeks in the city, he came back to the Verdigris valley. He seemed very nervous and was unable to work. He soon disappeared from the valley and was never heard from again.

Wallis and Maria Sophia Haskin's Children
Back from left to right: Florence, Mercedes, and Elmer.
Middle from left to right: Gerdula and Julius.
Front: Walter.
Haskin Family Photo.

Chapter 14   Legacy

By the end of 1889, the settlers of Mars and Jessup learned that the railroad, which they hoped would run through the valley, would not be constructed, after all. Instead, a short line was to be built between Sioux City, Iowa and O'Neill, Nebraska. Disappointed that the railroad had bypassed Jessup by four miles, many families moved from the valley to be closer to the rails. Soon, a new settlement, named Savage, formed near the rail line, one mile south of Royal.

As the village of Jessup struggled with the throes of death, Samuel Haskin struggled with his own demons. The death of Joseph Kibbee left him depressed and lethargic. He rented his store to Henry Charles, who also ran the Jessup Store, after purchasing it from Pete O'Malley. Then, Samuel turned the farm work over to Wallis and turned the stables over to Peter Brown.

Without the burdens of the farm, stables, and store, Samuel had more time to enjoy his family and his grandchildren. In February, he was thrilled to welcome a new granddaughter. Eva Annice was born to Wallis and Maria Sophia on February 17th, and she was their eighth child.

Slowly, winter released its icy grip on the hills of Mars and, once again, birds and blossoms flourished across the land.

That summer, Samuel purchased a stone monument and placed it at the grave of Joseph Kibbee. He still maintained contact with Joseph's widow, Sylvia, and learned that she gave birth in April to a little girl named Lillian Grace. Samuel had to chuckle because, in the end, Joseph got his wish. The baby was not named "Samuel."

The arrival of autumn heralded the marriage of Edwin Haskin to Alice Smith at Aten, Nebraska. Edwin and Alice made their home in Creighton with Alice's daughter, Mary, and Edwin's daughters, Cora and Millie. Edwin's sons, Spencer and Clarence, remained on the homestead near Mars.

A few days after Edwin's marriage, Samuel learned that

Mon-e-ga-he and his people were leaving the Verdigris River valley. The government allowed them to purchase some land west of Niobrara. Samuel was glad that the Ponca were allowed some land of their own, but he hated to see them leave. Mon-e-ga-he had been a close friend for many years and Samuel was going to miss him. Shon-ge-ska, however, told Samuel that he was going to remain in the hills and valleys of Mars, because he did not think that he could live without Maria Sophia Haskin's fresh pies.

Samuel remembered very well just how frightened Maria Sophia had been of the Ponca when she first came with her husband into the valley. Over the years, however, she had grown accustomed to having Shon-ge-ska and his people around. She even began baking pies, especially for Shon-ge-ska, and every time he came to visit, she insisted that he stay for supper. Samuel had to laugh at the sight of Wallis and Maria Sophia's children trying to follow their Ponca friend when he would leave their cabin. They would always lose him because he was a true woodsman, and would just disappear into the trees.

In the summer of 1891, Maria Sophia Haskin's brother, Charley Brandt took his family back to LaValle, Wisconsin. They returned to the cabin that Fred Brandt built in 1870. Charley was only six years old when his family moved into the new cabin and he lived there until his parents moved to Nebraska in 1881. The Brandts still owned the place, and Charley and Fannie were going to stay at the cabin during their stay in Wisconsin.

Most of Fred and Sophia Brandt's children were now married. Fred, Jr. married Florence Jacobs in 1885 and Emma Brandt married Florence's brother, Edwin, in 1886. Then in 1888, Anna Brandt married Lewis Woolman. Mary Brandt was never allowed back into her father's house. She moved out of the dugout, where she lived with her daughter and her mother, when she married Riley Brown. After Mary left, her mother, Sophia, moved back in with Fred and they took care of Mary's daughter, Maude.

Maria Sophia never reconciled with her sister, Mary. Furthermore, she did not want young Maude anywhere near the Wallis Haskin place. Maria Sophia just could not forgive her sister over the affair with Wallis, and she viewed Maude as a painful reminder of Mary's misbehavior.

Samuel's health continued to deteriorate through 1891. It soon became apparent to him that he was facing his own mortality. Through it all, however, Samuel began to see the purpose of his life and the ghosts of Raviah and Annie no longer tortured him. In his grandchildren, he clearly saw his legacy and a future that was brightened by the sacrifices he had made. Now, more than ever, he needed to be certain that his legacy would pass on down through the generations to come. Therefore, in December, Samuel made out his last will and testament.

"I Samuel Haskin being of sound mind and memory do give devise and bequeath all my property both real and personal to

"All realestate to W. R. Haskins

"All farming tools and all other tools except one mower to W. R. Haskins

"100 bushell of oats and 50 of corn one rone bull to W. R. Haskins

"And one sorrel horse and one red cow and one third of the hay on the primises to W. R. Haskin my youngest son

"One black mare colt 2 years old and one spoted cow to E. R. Haskins my oldest son

"All the corn on the premises belonging to me except 100 bushell and the 50 bushell before mentioned and all the oats except the 100 bushell before mentioned all the wheat belonging to me on the premises all the potatoes and provision to my present wife Charlott M. Haskins

"All household goods I had by my first wife to be divided up among the children of W. R. Haskins

"Hereby revoking all former wills by me made in witness whareof I Samuel Haskins have to this my last will and testament

subscribe by name this 18th day of December 1891

/s/ Samuel Haskin

    "Subscribed by the testator in the presence of each of us and at the same time declared by him to us to be his last will and testament and therefore we at the request of the testator and in his presence sign our names hereto as witnesses this 18th day of December 1891

/s/ Turner Gardner Mars Knox Co Neb

/s/ George S. Downey Mars Knox Co Neb"

    As the rays of the morning sun danced upon the flowing waters of the Verdigris River on January 7th, 1892, Samuel Haskin's sons and his wife stood at his bedside. Shortly before noon, Samuel opened his eyes for the last time and looked into the sad faces of his family. Then, the faces began to fade and darkness fell upon the valley.

    Samuel's trials were now over. Through joys and pains, he wove a future for his family. Through courage and perseverance, he paved the way for settlement in a harsh and unforgiving land. Through loss and sorrow, he created a solid foundation of lasting hope. The Haskin Homestead became his legacy, and the hills of Mars would echo his name for generations to come.

    And so the story continues *Beyond the Hills of Mars . . . .*

FAMILY TREE GLOSSARY
(Births Listed Through December 31, 1891)

Samuel and Annie Woodling Haskin

Raviah Lamora Haskin Rabuck	Born- June 14, 1844
Edwin Ruthvan Haskin	Born – February 18, 1846
Wallis Rowland Haskin	Born – August 12, 1854
Nancy Ann Bailey, Adopted	Born – 1853
August Meyer, Adopted	Born – 1856
Elizabeth Meyer, Adopted	Born – 1864

Frederick Rabuck and Raviah Haskin Rabuck

Delphine Lamora Rabuck	Born – January 11, 1860
Lenora Amelia Rabuck	Born – January 13, 1862
George Almon Rabuck	Born – November 29, 1864
Emma Phoebe Rabuck	Born – November 11, 1866
Frederick Ruthvon Rabuck	Born – December 12, 1868
Samuel Henry Rabuck	Born – December 23, 1870
William Wallace Rabuck	Born – February 9, 1872

Edwin Ruthvan Haskin and Delia Sherman Haskin

Spencer Carlyle Haskin	Born – September 22, 1865
Anna Haskin Goodman	Born – June 9, 1868
Clarence Haskin	Born – 1874
Millie May Haskin	Born – April 11, 1875
Cora Edith Haskin	Born – February 17, 1878

Fredrick Brandt and Sophia Rabuck Brandt

Maria Sophia Brandt Haskin	Born – October 5, 1858
Sara Caroline Brandt Gardner	Born – December 20, 1859
Fredrick August Brandt	Born – May 25, 1861
Carl (Charley) Henry Brandt	Born – May 26, 1864
Marie (Mary) Christann Brandt	Born – December 10, 1865
Emma Christina Brandt	Born – April 17, 1867
John Arnold Brandt	Born – February 4, 1869
Anna Doretta Brandt	Born – September 2, 1870

Dorothy Katherine Elizabeth Brandt   Born – January 14, 1873
Edward Brandt   Born – October 1, 1877

Wallis Rowland Haskin and Maria Sophia Brandt Haskin
Mercedes Adelia Haskin   Born – September 27, 1876
Florence Augusta Haskin   Born – December 24, 1877
Elmer Francis Haskin   Born – February 8, 1880
Gerdula May Haskin   Born – January 5, 1882
Julius Eugene Haskin   Born – August 23, 1884
Walter Clarence Haskin   Born – May 7, 1886
Blanche Ellen Haskin   Born – February 4, 1888
Eva Annice Haskin   Born – February 17, 1890

Cyrus Carver and Mary Carver
Dor Carver   Born – 1851
Shib Carver   Born – 1858
Loren Carver   Born – 1862
Oliver Carver   Born – 1864
Donaley Carver   Born – 1866
Barton Carver   Born – 1868
Orland Carver   Born – 1870

Louis Morsett and Philomone Morsett
Julius Morsett   Born – August 1, 1863
Mary Louisa Morsett   Born – January 12, 1867
Julia Ann Morsett   Born – December 19, 1869
Jeanette Loretta Morsett   Born – January 19, 1871
Elizabeth Morsett   Born – May 17, 1875
Margaret Amelia Morsett   Born – April 28, 1877
Johnnie Morsett   Born – April 28, 1877
Joseph Morsett   Born – September 3, 1878
Frank Morsett   Born – March 15, 1881
Rose Wilheminia Morsett   Born – October 15, 1882
Charley Fred Morsett   Born – May 9, 1884

Lucious Kibbee and Hanna Kibbee

Joseph Kibbee   Born – 1863
Minerva Kibbee   Born – 1865
Freeman (Frank) Kibbee   Born – 1868
Emily Kibbee   Born – 1871

Joseph Kibbee and Sylvia Sherman Kibbee

Sylvia Bell Kibbee   Born – August 3, 1885
Alta May Kibbee   Born – April 8, 1887
Lillian Grace Kibbee   Born – April 26, 1890

The Wallis Haskin Family in 1892
Standing in back from left to right: Gerdula, Mercedes,
Florence, Elmer, and Julius.
In the middle from left to right; Wallis holding baby Oscar
(born after Samuel Haskin died), Walter, and Maria Sophia
holding Eva.
Seated in front: Blanche.
Haskin Family Photo.

GLOSSARY OF PEOPLE AND PLACES

Adams, A. E. – A farmer near Walnut Grove; Charlotte Brown's son, Robert, was bonded to Adams to pay his father's debt.

Arrow Chief – Mon-e-ga-he, leader of the Ponca band that remained in the Verdigris River Valley.

Bailey, Nancy Ann – Adopted daughter of Samuel and Annie Haskin.

Baraboo River Valley – The valley in Wisconsin where the Haskins, Brandts, and Rabucks lived.

Bierd, Mary Belinda – Frederick Rabuck's second wife.

Big Sioux River – A river separating Iowa from the Dakota Territory.

Brandt, Charley – Brother of Maria Sophia Brandt Haskin and son of Fredrick and Sophia Brandt.

Brandt, Fannie – Fannie Burton became the wife of Charley Brandt.

Brandt, Fredrick – A German immigrant that settled in LaValle, Wisconsin and married Sophia Rabuck; father of Maria Sophia Brandt Haskin.

Brandt, Maria Sophia – The daughter of Fredrick and Sophia Brandt and wife of Wallis Haskin.

Brandt, Mary – A younger sister to Maria Sophia Brandt Haskin and a daughter of Fredrick and Sophia Brandt; mother of Maude Brandt.

Brandt, Maude – The daughter if Mary Brandt, it is presumed that Wallis Haskin was Maude's father.

Brandt, Sophia – Sophia Rabuck Brandt, the sister of Frederick Rabuck and the wife of Fredrick Brandt.

Brill, A. J. – The husband of Media Williams Brill, who was the daughter of Julia Griffith.

Brooks, George – A businessman from Bazile Mills who convinced the Government to move the Jessup Post Office from the Knox/Antelope county line to a location two miles to the south and near Julius Hering's flour mill.

Brown, Charlotte – Charlotte DeBoe, the wife of John Brown, also the fourth wife of Samuel Haskin.

Brown, Henrietta – Daughter of John and Charlotte Brown and wife of John Strope.

Brown, John – A farmer near Walnut Grove and husband of Charlotte Brown.

Brown, Peter – A son of John and Charlotte Brown; Peter moved in with Samuel and Charlotte after they were married.

Brown, Robert – A son of John and Charlotte Brown.

Burton, Fannie – Wife of Charley Brandt; Fannie was one of the teachers of the Mars School.

Burton, Viola – The first teacher at the Jessup School.

Carver, Barton – Son of Cyrus and Mary Carver.

Carver, Cyrus – A longtime friend of Samuel Haskin; Cyrus settled near Samuel on the Verdigris River in Nebraska.

Carver, Dor – Son of Cyrus and Mary Carver.

Carver, Loren – Son of Cyrus and Mary Carver.

Carver, Mary – Wife of Cyrus Carver.

Carver, Orland – Son of Cyrus and Mary Carver.

Carver, Shib – Son of Cyrus and Mary Carver.

Chicago, Nebraska – A small settlement about sixteen miles to the north and east of Neligh and about 12 miles south and west of Creighton.

Coming Moon – Ta-in-ge, a name that the Ponca gave to Maria Sophia Haskin.

Creighton, Nebraska – A town almost fifteen miles east of Mars.

Crescent Moon – Mi-ta-in, a name that the Ponca gave to Annie Haskin.

Crum, Del – Delphine Rabuck Crum Lamphere was a granddaughter of Samuel and Annie Haskin and the oldest daughter of Frederick Rabuck and Raviah Haskin Rabuck.

Crum, Elroy – The first husband of Delphine Rabuck.

Crum, Frank – Son of Elroy and Del Crum.

Crum, Walter – Son of Elroy and Del Crum.

Dalrymple, Elizabeth – Elizabeth VanDeBogert Fields

Dalrymple Haskin was the second wife of Samuel Haskin.

Dull Knife – A Cheyenne chief who helped a band of Indians escape from a reservation in Oklahoma, Dull Knife and his band fled north while raiding, looting, and murdering any white settlers who crossed his path.

Fay, Amelia – A woman whose family settled at Mars, just east of Shib Carver, Amelia served as a witness to the codicil of Julia Haskin's last will and testament.

Ferryville, Wisconsin – A town in western Wisconsin on the banks of the Mississippi River, Samuel Haskin and his scouts passed through this town on their way to Nebraska.

Fields, Charles – A son of Elizabeth VanDeBogert Fields Dalrymple Haskin, Charles lived with his mother in Neligh.

Fields, Elizabeth – Elizabeth VanDeBogert Fields Dalrymple Haskin was the second wife of Samuel Haskin.

Fields, Will – Jerome Sharpe's hired man.

Glenalpine, Nebraska – A settlement nearly nine miles southwest of Mars; the Lucious Kibbee family lived near Glenalpine.

Goodman, Anna – Anna Haskin Goodman is the daughter of Edwin R. Haskin and Delia Sherman Haskin, she married George Goodman.

Goodman, George – Brother of Katie Goodman and husband of Anna Haskin Goodman.

Goodman, Katie – Sister of George Goodman; Katie worked at a hotel in Creighton and kept house for Julia Griffith at the Mars boarding house; Katie moved in with Samuel Haskin after Julia died.

Goodman, Mary Ellen – Daughter of Katie Goodman.

Great Turtle – Ke-ton-ga, the name given to Samuel Haskin by the Ponca.

Griffith, Julia – Julia Griffith Haskin, wife of William Griffith, the third wife of Samuel Haskin; mother of Media Brill; Julia operated the boarding house at Mars.

Griffith, William – A close friend of Samuel Haskin and the husband of Julia Griffith.

Grimton, Nebraska – A small settlement about six miles north of Venus.

Haskin, Alice – Alice Smith Haskin was the second wife of Edwin R. Haskin.

Haskin, Anna – Anna Haskin Goodman is the daughter of Edwin R. Haskin and Delia Sherman Haskin; Anna married George Goodman.

Haskin, Annie – First wife of Samuel Haskin and mother of Raviah, Edwin, and Wallis.

Haskin, Blanche – Daughter of Wallis and Maria Sophia Haskin.

Haskin, Charlotte – Charlotte DeBoe Brown Haskin was the fourth wife of Samuel Haskin; Charlotte was the mother of Henrietta Strope, Robert Brown, and Peter Brown; wife of John Brown.

Haskin, Clarence – Son of Edwin R. Haskin and Delia Sherman Haskin.

Haskin, Cora – Daughter of Edwin R. Haskin and Delia Sherman Haskin.

Haskin, Delia – Delia Sherman Haskin was the wife of Edwin R. Haskin and a sister to Watts and Tite Sherman.

Haskin, Edwin – Edwin R. Haskin, son of Samuel and Annie Haskin and husband of Delia Sherman Haskin.

Haskin, Elizabeth – Elizabeth VanDeBogert Fields Dalrymple Haskin, the second wife of Samuel Haskin.

Haskin, Elmer – Son of Wallis and Maria Sophia Haskin.

Haskin, Eva – Daughter of Wallis and Maria Sophia Haskin.

Haskin, Florence – Daughter of Wallis and Maria Sophia Haskin.

Haskin, Gerdula – Daughter of Wallis and Maria Sophia Haskin.

Haskin, Julia – Julia Griffith Haskin, wife of William Griffith and third wife of Samuel Haskin, she operated the boarding house at Mars, she was the mother of Media Brill.

Haskin, Julius – Son of Wallis and Maria Sophia Haskin.

Haskin, Maria Sophia – Maria Sophia Brandt Haskin, daughter of Fredrick and Sophia Brandt and wife of Wallis Haskin.

Haskin, Mercedes – Oldest child of Wallis and Maria Sophia Haskin.

Haskin, Millie – Daughter of Edwin and Delia Haskin

Haskin, Raviah – Raviah Haskin Rabuck was the daughter of Samuel and Annie Haskin and wife of Frederick Rabuck.

Haskin, Samuel – Husband of Annie Haskin and father of Raviah, Edwin, and Wallis; Samuel paved the way for settlement in the Verdigris River Valley.

Haskin, Spencer – Oldest child of Edwin and Delia Haskin.

Haskin, Sydney – Brother of Samuel Haskin; Sydney settled on some land in eastern Antelope County near Plainview.

Haskin, Wallis – Son of Samuel and Annie Haskin and husband of Maria Sophia Brandt Haskin.

Haskin, Walter – Son of Wallis and Maria Sophia Haskin.

He of the Earth – Mon-ka-ta, a member of the Ponca band that lived in the Verdigris River Valley.

Hering, Julius – A millwright from Germany who built a flour mill on the banks of the Verdigris River.

Hering's Mill – The Jessup Roller Mills built by a German millwright named Julius Hering on the banks of the Verdigris River, two miles south of Mars.

Hubbard, Annis – Daughter of Cynthia Jane Parks Hubbard and niece to Sylvanius Whitmore's wife.

Hubbard, Arthur – Son of Cynthia Jane Parks Hubbard and nephew to Sylvanius Whitmore's wife.

Hubbard, Cynthia – Cynthia Jane Parks Hubbard was the sister of Octavia Parks Whitmore and a widow who brought her three children to Antelope County in 1886; Cynthia filed claim to a homestead south of Mars.

Hubbard, Edmond – Son of Cynthia Jane Parks Hubbard and nephew to Sylvanius Whitmore's wife; Edmond was named after his father, Edmond Hubbard, Sr., who died of injuries received in the Civil War.

Ironton, Wisconsin – The place where Samuel Haskin first settled when he moved to Wisconsin; Wallis Haskin's birthplace.

Jackson, Andrew – A saloon keeper in LaValle, Wisconsin and a close friend of Samuel Haskin.

Jessup, Nebraska – The original name of the post office and the settlement on the Knox / Antelope county line; Jessup was moved two miles south, near Hering's Mill, in 1885.

Jessup Roller Mills – A flour mill on the Verdigris River, two miles south of Mars, built by Julius Hering.

Joerissen, Charles – The first postmaster of Mars; Charles Joerissen and his family moved to the Verdigris River Valley in 1883 and settled on land that was just north of Samuel Haskin's homestead.

Joerissen, Christiana – Wife of Charles Joerissen.

Jones, Andrew – A settler near Walnut Grove; Charlotte Brown became bond servant to Andrew to pay a debt owed by her husband.

Jones, Ben – A settler near the Jessup Roller Mills; Ben took in an ailing stranger named Johnny Moore.

Ke-ton-ga – Great Turtle, the name given to Samuel Haskin by the Ponca.

Ke-zhin-ga – Little Turtle, the name given to Wallis Haskin by the Ponca.

Kibbee, Emily – Youngest child of Lucious and Hanna Kibbee.

Kibbee, Frank – Youngest son of Lucious and Hanna Kibbee.

Kibbee, Hanna – Wife of Lucious Kibbee.

Kibbee, Joseph – Oldest son of Lucious and Hanna Kibbee and Samuel Haskin's hired man.

Kibbee, Lucious – A settler who filed claim on land at Glenalpine; Lucious was the father of Joseph and Frank Kibbee.

Kibbee, Minerva – Oldest daughter of Lucious and Hanna Kibbee.

Koehler, Emma – Foster daughter of Charles and Christianna Joerissen; Emma was the same age as Mercedes Haskin.

Lamphere, Charles – The man Delphine Rabuck Crum married after she moved to Dakota Territory.

Lamphere, Del - Delphine Rabuck Crum Lamphere was a granddaughter of Samuel and Annie Haskin and the oldest daughter of Frederick Rabuck and Raviah Haskin Rabuck.

LaValle, Wisconsin – Originally called Marsten, was a town in Wisconsin where Samuel and Annie Haskin lived before they moved to Nebraska; The Haskins ran the general store at LaValle.

Little Turtle – Ke-zhin-ga, the name given to Wallis Haskin by the Ponca.

Little Wolf – A Cheyenne Chief who helped a band of Indians escape from a reservation in Oklahoma; the Cheyenne fled north raiding, looting, and murdering any whites that crossed their path.

Lockwood, Bert – The young man who shot Will Fields behind the Jessup Store, supposedly by accident.

Mars, Nebraska – A small settlement on the Knox and Antelope county line, initially named Jessup, but changed its name to Mars when the Jessup post office contract was moved to a location two miles to the south; home of Samuel Haskin.

Mason City, Iowa – A town in northern Iowa, which was on the route, Samuel Haskin traveled from Wisconsin to Nebraska.

McCollum, Alexander – The first postmaster of Jessup; he lived ½ mile west of Samuel Haskin on the Knox and Antelope county line.

McCollum, Evaline – Wife of Alexander McCollum.

Meyer, August – Adopted son of Samuel and Annie Haskin; brother of Elizabeth Meyer.

Meyer, Elizabeth – Adopted daughter of Samuel and Annie Haskin; sister of August Meyer.

Middleton, Doc – A horse thief rumored to be stealing horses in the Millerboro area.

Millerboro, Nebraska – A small settlement five miles east of

Mars.

Mi-ta-in – Crescent Moon, the name given to Annie Haskin by the Ponca.

Mon-ka-ta – He of the Earth, a member of the Ponca band that lived in the Verdigris River Valley.

Mon-e-ga-he – Arrow Chief, the leader of the small band of Ponca that lived and hunted in the Verdigris River Valley.

Moore, Johnny – An ailing drifter who was taken in by Ben Jones; the first person buried in the Carver Cemetery.

Morrill, Moses – Moses brought his family from Iowa in the mid 1880's and settled on some land west of Charles Joerissen.

Morsett, Charley – Youngest son of Louis and Philomone Morsett.

Morsett, Jeanette – Daughter of Louis and Philomone Morsett.

Morsett, Joseph – Son of Louis and Philomone Morsett.

Morsett, Louis – A Frenchman who Samuel Haskin met while shipping supplies from Niobrara; Louis homesteaded some land west of Alexander McCollum.

Morsett, Philomone – Wife of Louis Morsett.

Neligh, Nebraska – A town on the Elkhorn River in Antelope County; during the 1880's, the Antelope County Courthouse was located in Neligh.

Niobrara, Nebraska – A town on the Missouri River; County Seat of Knox County and location of the land office for

Northeast Nebraska.

Oakdale, Nebraska – A town on the Elkhorn River, east of Neligh, in Antelope County; County Seat of Antelope County.

Rabuck, Del - Delphine Rabuck Crum Lamphere was a granddaughter of Samuel and Annie Haskin and the oldest daughter of Frederick Rabuck and Raviah Haskin Rabuck

Rabuck, Frederick – Husband of Raviah Haskin Rabuck; father of Delphine Rabuck Crum Lamphere; brother of Sophia Rabuck Brandt.

Rabuck, Sophia - Sophia Rabuck Brandt, the sister of Frederick Rabuck and the wife of Fredrick Brandt.

Rabuck, William – Older brother of Sophia Rabuck Brandt and Frederick Rabuck; William immigrated from Germany and settled near Marston, Wisconsin.

Redfield, Dakota – A town in the Dakota Territory where Frederick Rabuck took his family when they left Wisconsin.

Reedstown, Wisconsin – A town in Wisconsin, between LaValle and Ferryville, that Samuel Haskin traveled through on his way from Wisconsin to Nebraska.

Royal, Nebraska – A small settlement consisting of a post office and a store, about six miles south of Mars.

Savage, Nebraska – A small settlement that began around 1890 about seven miles south of Mars and a little over a mile south of Royal.

Sharpe, Jerome – A farmer who owned land in Knox County northwest of Mars; Jerome organized a vigilante group to search for Doc Middleton.

Sherman, Belle – Daughter of Watts Sherman and a teacher at the Verdigris Creek School near Mars.

Sherman, Delia – First wife of Edwin R. Haskin; sister of Watts and Tite Sherman.

Sherman, Jennie – Daughter of Watts Sherman and a teacher at the Mars School.

Sherman, Sylvia – Daughter of William Sherman; wife of Joseph Kibbee.

Sherman, Tite – Brother of Delia Sherman Haskin; Tite filed claim to land near the Jessup Roller Mills.

Sherman, Watts – Brother of Delia Sherman Haskin; Watts owned land near his brother Tite.

Sherman, William – An early homesteader of Antelope County who filed claim to some land south of the Wallis Haskin homestead; father of Sylvia Sherman Kibbee.

Shon-ge-ska – White Wolf, a member of the band of Ponca that lived in the Verdigris River Valley; a close friend of Wallis Haskin.

Smith, Mary – Daughter of Alice Smith Haskin; stepdaughter of Edwin R. Haskin.

St. Paul Junction, Iowa – A town in northern Iowa that Samuel Haskin traveled through on his way from Wisconsin to Nebraska.

Strope, Henrietta – Daughter of John and Charlotte Brown;

wife of John Strope.

Strope, John – A farmer who settled on some land near Walnut Grove; husband of Henrietta Brown Strope.

Ta-in-ge – Coming Moon, a name that the Ponca gave to Maria Sophia Haskin.

VanOstrand, George – A farmer who purchased some land near Pleasant Valley; George was one of Katie Goodman's suitors and eventually, Katie went to live with him.

VanOstrand, Jeremiah – Jeremiah built bridges in the area; son of George VanOstrand.

Venus, Nebraska – A settlement seven miles west of Mars; named by Sylvanius Whitmore because of the beauty of the surrounding countryside.

Verdigris River – A creek that begins in Antelope County and flows north through Knox County and empties into the Niobrara River; the name Verdigris is French and describes the brownish green color of the creek;

Walnut Grove, Nebraska – A settlement in Knox County, north and east of Venus; Walnut Grove is located near the Middle Branch of the Verdigris River.

Westfield, Iowa – A town on the Big Sioux River in northwestern Iowa; Samuel Haskin traveled through an abandoned Westfield on his way to Nebraska from Wisconsin.

White Wolf – Shon-ge-ska, a member of the band of Ponca that lived in the Verdigris River Valley; a close friend of Wallis Haskin.

Whitmore, Helen – Daughter of Sylvanius and Octavia Whitmore.

Whitmore, Henrietta – Daughter of Sylvanius and Octavia Whitmore.

Whitmore, Octavia – Octavia Parks Whitmore, wife of Sylvanius Whitmore and sister of Cynthia Parks Hubbard.

Whitmore, Sylvanius L. – A settler from Vermont who founded and named the town of Venus.

Williams, Media – Media Williams Brill, daughter of Julia Griffith.

Yankton, Dakota – A town in the Dakota Territory on the Missouri River; Samuel Haskin traveled through Yankton on his way to Nebraska from Wisconsin; a river town from which Samuel Haskin and other settlers from northeast Nebraska would purchase their supplies.

The Mail Wagon at the Mars Post Office
Photo taken about 1890
In front seat from left to right: Edwin Haskin and Samuel
Haskin.
In back seat from left to right: Charlotte Haskin and Alice
Haskin.
Haskin Family Photo.

Edwin Haskin's Children

Back from left to right: Spencer and Clarence.
Middle from left to right: Millie, Anna, and Cora.
Front: Mary Smith (Alice Haskin's daughter from her first
marriage). Haskin Family Photo, 1891.

The Verdigris River
Photo by D. R. Haskin

North ↑

Niobrara

Verdigre

rimton
Walnut Grove

Creighton

Venus   Mars   Millerboro

Glenalpine   Jessup

Royal   Chicago   Plainview

rchard   Savage (1890)   Willowdale

Frenchtown

Glendale

Clearwater

Neligh

Area Map
A sketch of the towns and settlements of Knox, Antelope, and western Pierce Counties from the mid 1880's to 1890.
Map not drawn to scale.

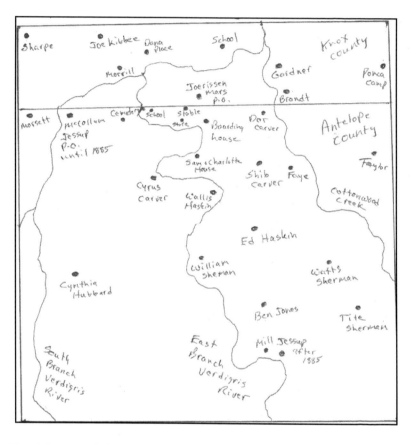

Residents of the Mars and Jessup vicinity in the 1880's.
A sketch showing the homes of the settlers of the region.
Map not drawn to scale.

Book Orders

The Hills Of Mars, by D. R. Haskin, may be purchased by sending a check or money order for $15.95/book, plus $5.00 shipping and handling (1 or 2 books), along with your name and address to:

> D. R. Haskin
> 86951   519 Ave.
> Royal, NE 68773

*Orders of 3 to 6 books, please add $10.00 for shipping and handling.

Historic Mars Wildlife Area and Campground

Want to get away from it all for a few days? Historic Mars Wildlife Area and Campground offers campsites along the beautiful Verdigris Creek. Bring your tents, trailer campers, or RV's to camp at Samuel Haskin's Homestead at Mars. Located 6.5 miles north of Royal, Nebraska.

Electric hook-ups are available on a first-come, first-serve basis.

Visitors can hike through the wildlife area to view: beaver, deer, hawks, turkeys, rabbits, raccoons, eagles, and other wildlife that make their home in the hills of Mars.

Rates: $10.00 per campsite per night without electric hook-up. $15.00 per campsite per night with electric hook-up.

Call 402-847-3415 to make reservations for camping.

Tour Mars

Take a guided tour through the hills of Mars. Stand in the Shib Carver dugout, see the Mars Stable, view Samuel Haskin's dugout, walk along the old wagon trails, and hear the stories of the families who lived at Mars in the 1880's.

There is a nominal fee for the guided tour. To arrange a tour of Mars, call 402-847-3415.